P9-DDV-818

I AM CANADA

PRISONER OF DIEPPE

World War II

by Hugh Brewster

Scholastic Canada Ltd.

Toronto New York London Auckland Sydney
Mexico City New Delhi Hong Kong Buenos Aires

Copyright © 2010 by Hugh Brewster. All rights reserved.

A Dear Canada Book. Published by Scholastic Canada Ltd.
SCHOLASTIC and I AM CANADA and logos are trademarks
and/or registered trademarks of Scholastic Inc.

Library and Archives Canada Cataloguing in Publication

Brewster, Hugh
Prisoner of Dieppe : WWII / Hugh Brewster.

(I am Canada)
ISBN 978-0-545-98594-9

1. Dieppe Raid, 1942--Juvenile fiction. 2. Canada--Armed Forces--
History--World War, 1939-1945--Juvenile fiction. 3. Prisoners of
war--Canada--Juvenile fiction. 4. World War, 1939-1945--Prisoners and
prisons, German--Juvenile fiction. 5. World War, 1939-1945--Canada--
Juvenile fiction. I. Title. II. Series: I am Canada

PS8603.R49P75 2010   jC813'.6   C2010-901709-9

6 5 4 3 2 1   Printed in Canada 114   10 11 12 13 14

The display type was set in Dirty Headline.
The text was set in Minion.

First printing June 2010

To Ron Reynolds, who was there

PROLOGUE

May 26, 1996

Dear Lachlan:

It was you who started this.

I'm sure you remember that school project — was it Grade Five or Six? — when you came over to the house with your dad's video camera and made me talk about the war. I told your grandmother I didn't want to do it but she wouldn't hear of it. She reminded me that I was always saying the younger generation needed to know what war was really like. Said it might even give me some "closure."

"Closure," I thought to myself. If only it were that easy. There won't be any of that till I close my eyes for the last time. . . .

Well, Lachlan, I promised your grandmother before she died that I would write it all down. So here, in my own words, is what I remember of what happened on that terrible morning of August 19, 1942, on the

1

beaches of a French town called Dieppe. And on all the miserable days that followed. You're the only family member who is interested in this. You're also now the age I was when I went to war. Maybe that will help you understand how it was for me, my friend Mackie, and the others. Maybe you can understand why it had to happen.

I don't think I ever will.

Your loving grandpa,

Alistair Morrison

CHAPTER 1

ON HIAWATHA ROAD

June 14, 1929

"You're the new Limeys, eh?"

Some older boys had gathered by the swings where I was pushing my little sister, Elspeth. My mother had sent us to the park at the bottom of the street since she was busy unpacking trunks and boxes in our new house.

"You're the *new Limeys, eh?*" the biggest boy said again, a little louder. I found his Canadian accent hard to follow.

"Beg pardon?" I responded.

"Beg pa-a*rr*-don?" the boys repeated, elbowing each other as they imitated my Scottish burr.

"I'm no a Limey," I said, holding the swing still and putting an arm over Elspeth's shoulder. "We're not English. We're Scots!"

"Well, Scottie dog," said the biggest boy, chewing hard on his gum as his pals circled around us. "Maybe they didn't tell you. This park's just for *Canadians!* You forgot to ask *us* for permission!"

With that he pushed me down and started twisting the chains on the swing. Elspeth screamed as the chains wrapped around her head. I jumped up and charged at him but another boy grabbed me and pushed me down again.

All of a sudden, out of nowhere, I heard a high-pitched war whoop. A red-faced boy charged at the bully and head-butted him in the stomach. With a howl he fell down in the sand while Elspeth quickly unwound in the swing. His three buddies ran to his side and picked him up. Then, muttering threats, they left.

Our rescuer helped Elspeth down and asked me if I was okay. I nodded. Then he said, "I'm Mackie. I'm Scotch, too. Though I never been there."

"I'm Alistair, and this is Elspeth. We're from Glasgow," I replied. Then I added, "My mum says Scotch is a drink and that you ought to say 'Scottish.'"

"Okay, then." Mackie grinned. "We're all Scott-*ish*, and the Scott-*ish* should stick together!"

I blushed, realizing I shouldn't be correcting this older boy who had come to our rescue. "Scots wha hae!" I suddenly blurted out, repeating the first words of the Scottish anthem.

"Scots wha hae!" Mackie said, flashing his big smile. "I live on Hiawatha, too," he continued, "just down the street. We saw you folks move in yesterday."

He walked us back across the park and up the street to the wooden steps in front of our porch. Then, with a wave, he was gone.

I'd like to tell you that Mackie and I were fast friends from that day onwards. But it never happened that way. He was two years older than me, which is a big difference when you're a kid. And he went to the Catholic school while I went to the public school, so we walked in different directions. He'd often wave at me and say with a wink, "Hey, kid, Scots wha hae!"

I knew his brothers and sisters, too, since everybody on Hiawatha knew their neighbours. When we first arrived from Scotland, my mother couldn't get over how friendly they all were. In Scotland, you had to be introduced to people first, but in Canada they dropped by with a pie, or jam, or maybe butter tarts — a new treat.

People on our street became even closer once the Depression hit. All of a sudden, it seemed like everyone's father was out of work, including ours. My dad had come over from Scotland a year ahead of us and had found a good job at the Massey-Harris tractor plant. But soon farmers couldn't afford new tractors. We heard that on the Prairies the fields had turned into dust bowls as the dry soil blew away because of drought. So my father and hundreds of others at the plant were laid off. Every day he would go off looking for work and come home tired and discouraged. Soon he just sat in our front room or on the porch in his undershirt, smoking and reading the newspaper. My parents thought about going back to Scotland, but our relatives told us things were no better there.

During those bleak years, no jobs meant no money — some people even had to line up for food at the soup kitchen on Queen Street. Mackie's family was hit particularly hard. The McAllisters had six children and Mackie's dad just couldn't find work. For a while, he tried selling brushes door-to-door, but I think he found it humiliating. Then we heard he had gone out west to look for work. But he never came back. Mackie's older brother Colin dropped out of school and found labouring jobs to help out. Mackie and his younger brother had a morning paper route and Mackie delivered groceries by bicycle after school. My mother always made sure Mackie's mom got baskets of vegetables from our garden, even though I knew she didn't like Mrs. McAllister very much. I think my mother also looked down on the McAllisters a little because they were Roman Catholics — one of the prejudices she had brought with her from the old country.

Whenever she could scrape together a little extra money, my mother's favourite escape was to go to "the pictures," as she called the movies. The Rialto was our neighbourhood cinema and for 25 cents she could see the newsreels, previews, a short feature and a full-length movie. My favourite escape was the public library, which my Grade Two teacher had told me about. By the time I was twelve I'd read all the books in the children's section, so the librarian, Mrs. Newman, let me take books from the adult shelves, as long as she looked them over first. I remember lying reading on our porch swing when Mackie would wheel by on his grocery bicycle with a large box balanced on the carrier in front of the handlebars. "Hey, Bookboy!" he would call out and I would blush and wave.

After two years of high school, Mackie dropped out so he could help support his family. He usually had two or three jobs on the go at once, but he still had time to see his friends — he was very popular — and to play on a baseball team. When he was about seventeen, Mackie — who by then liked to be called Mack — got a job in the shipping department at Canada Packers. He soon developed broad shoulders and impressive arms from lifting heavy boxes. And his knife-parted black hair fell over his forehead in a way that made him look like Clark Gable in *It Happened One Night*. I remember when he would walk down our street in his sleeve-less undershirt, swinging his black lunch pail and whistling, my mother would call out, "Well, here comes Clark Gable!" and my two sisters would squeal and run to the front window.

When I was in Grade Ten, my father died. He had managed to get short-shift work back at the Massey-Harris plant, but his face seemed to get greyer by the day. As a soldier during the Great War, he had been gassed in Belgium and his lungs were never good after that. He shouldn't have smoked, but he did, quite heavily. When he came down with emphysema he got thinner and thinner and had terrible coughing fits until one day when I came home from school, my mother and sisters were weeping, and he was gone.

After the funeral, I told my mother that I would leave school and get a job, but she wouldn't hear of it. "No, son," she said, "you must finish your schooling. I'll see to that."

And she did. Within days, Mother had got a job as a trainee telephone operator with "the Bell" as she called it. And Elspeth, who didn't much like school, took a typing course and found secretarial work. (My youngest sister, Doreen, was still only in Grade Six.) I liked school, particularly History and English, and I wasn't bad at languages, though Math was always a bit of a struggle. My favourite history teacher asked me if I'd ever thought about going to university, but I knew there was no money for that. Boys from Rosedale went to university, not anyone from our neighbourhood.

In my second-last year of high school there was much talk about a war with Adolf Hitler's Germany. On the radio we would hear Hitler giving loud, ranting speeches while thousands chanted. *"Sieg Heil, Sieg Heil!"* Some people on our street thought Hitler wasn't so bad. They would say things like, "Well, at least with Hitler, everybody in Germany has a job!"

When Hitler invaded Poland in September of 1939 we knew that Great Britain would declare war on Germany. One week later, we gathered around the radio to hear Prime Minister Mackenzie King tell us that Canada, too, was now at war. It was a sombre moment.

Mackie's brother Colin was already in the militia. Within a few weeks we heard that he was going off to army camp before being sent overseas. After that, Mackie's mother depended on him even more. I know Mackie would have liked to take girls out dancing at the Palais Royale or to ride the roller coaster at Sunnyside, but he didn't have the money. He started dropping over for visits in the evenings — I think just to get out of the house. I was usually studying, but would always make time for him. It was very flattering that a popular athlete like Mackie wanted to spend time with a skinny bookworm like me. I guess it was because I could make him laugh. Sometimes, the things I said — even unintentionally — would send him into fits of laughter. He was one of those people who would laugh until he was out of breath. Then, all of a sudden, he'd say a quick "See you" and be gone.

The next summer, after I finished high school, I found a temporary job at Canada Packers, working on the labelling line. Mackie was still in the shipping department and we often took the streetcar home together. One day he mentioned getting a letter from Colin, who was already over in England. Colin had written that the English girls were "just crazy about the Canucks." They were expecting invasion by the Germans any day, and Colin was stationed on the south coast near a place called Hastings.

"Hastings!" I said. "That's where the Normans invaded in 1066! You know, William the Conquerer and all that."

"Oh-h, ok-a-ay, Bookboy," replied Mackie, flashing his big smile. "Whatever you say."

A few days later, Mackie said that if we went down to the Exhibition grounds we could find out what was involved in getting over to England.

"Are you thinking of joining up?" I asked.

"My mother would kill me," he replied. "But it can't hurt to find out about it. Why don't you come with me?"

I was always flattered when Mackie asked me to do anything with him, so I agreed. The next day, we took the streetcar along the lakefront to the huge, pillared gates of the Canadian National Exhibition. A visit to the Ex had always been a big summer treat for us as children — with free samples in the Food Building and sometimes a ticket to one of the rides on the Midway. Now, though, the Ex looked completely different, with khaki army trucks everywhere and men marching in columns. We saw a banner that said *Royal Regiment* on a building that had a lineup of young men in front of it. We joined the line and when we got inside the building were given forms to fill out.

"Wait a second," I said to Mackie, "These are *recruiting* forms. We're not joining up, are we? My mother will have a fit!"

"Oh come on, Allie," Mackie replied with a wink.

"How else are you gonna cut the apron strings? You'll be able to see the white cliffs of Dover, and Big Ben, and maybe your relatives in Scotland, too!"

Suddenly a big man in uniform bawled out, "Hurry up, you two, cut the chatter. You're holding up the line!"

We sat down at a long table. My heart was pounding. I looked over at Mackie, who was already filling out his form. For the first time, I saw that his real name was Hamish McTavish McAllister. (No wonder he preferred Mack or Mackie.) I wasn't crazy about the idea of joining the Army. Being yelled at and told what to do didn't appeal to me very much. But being yelled at by the foreman at Canada Packers wasn't much better. And it would be exciting to see London and all the places I'd read about in books.

And maybe I *would* get up to Glasgow to see my aunts and cousins. I could just remember the red sandstone tenement in Glasgow where we used to live.

I picked up the pen and began to print my name.

An hour or so later, we were standing in another line, this time in our underpants. At the front of the room was a doctor with a stethoscope giving each recruit a physical examination. I felt quite shy and pale and skinny, particularly standing behind Mackie, who was so brown and brawny. I must have dawdled when my turn came because an officer with a little waxed moustache bawled out, "Come on, Mr. Bones, move it! Maybe the Army will put some meat on you!" I blushed and scurried up to the doctor.

At the end of all the inspections, they formed us into a line and told us we were now "Royals" — members of the Royal Regiment of Canada. In a week, we had to report for training.

When we got outside, Mackie was jumping about. "Well, Allie, we did it! We did it!" Then, to the tune of the old war song "Tipperary," he sang, "Hello, Piccadilly, Goodbye old T.O. We're on our way to Piccadilly, So Allie, let's go!" and then burst out laughing. I laughed too, swept up in his exuberance. But I wasn't at all sure about what we'd just done. And I dreaded having to tell my mother.

"You've done *what?*" she exclaimed when I gave her the news. "What has that *Catholic* boy talked you into? I'll go and speak to his mother this *minute!*"

"Mother, we're not boys," I replied. "And it's too late, we've enlisted. And I'll be able to see Scotland and Auntie Lil and the cousins — "

"You won't be able to see *anyone* if you're *killed,* now will you? Have you thought about *that?*" She sat down heavily in a chair and then her features crumpled. She put her face down into her apron and cried in a way I'd never heard before, not even when my father died.

"Oh son, son, what have you done, what have you done?" she wailed between heaving sobs. "You don't know . . . you're not the army type . . . your dad was in the last one . . . look what it did to him . . . "

She fled to her room and slammed the door. The noise of her crying echoed through the whole house. At times it would die down and I would think of going to talk to her, but then it would start up again. My sisters crept around the house, casting dark glances at me.

It was very hard to see my mother so upset, but in a way it made it easier. I knew I had to escape from this house of women. I had to find my way in the world and become a man.

Or so I thought.

CHAPTER 2
CAMP BORDEN
August 12, 1940

I awoke early and, for a second, thought I was still in my bed at home. The sun's first rays shining through the speckled canvas of the tent made me feel happy. Then I remembered where I was and my heart sank. Camp Borden. And another day of basic training lay ahead. I was already stiff, sore and fed up, even though it was only our second week at the camp. My mother's warning, "You're not the army type," kept playing in my head. I'd shrugged it off at the time, but now I often wondered if she wasn't right.

I heard snuffles and snoring from a few of the seven other men stretched out in their sleeping bags around the central pole of the musty old tent. Then the first notes of the bugler playing "Reveille" sounded outside.

Tun-tun, ta-ra-rum, Tun-tun, ta-ra-rum, Tun-tun, ta-ra-rum, RA-RA-rum.

This was followed by the all-too-familiar voice of Sergeant-Major Kewley, our training instructor.

15

When I stuck my head out through the flaps, I could see Kewley strutting about between the tents, tapping on them with his sergeant's cane.

"Come on, boys, everybody up, up, UP. Let's go, go, GO. PT in five, outside, shorts only," he shouted in his morning incantation. "Get up, get out, get GOING!"

Kewley was strictly old-school British army. He had fought at the battle of the Somme in 1916, where, as he had told us in his strong English accent, "so many good men died — fifty thousand in the first bleedin' day."

I often wished that he had been one of them — because Sergeant-Major Kewley yelled at everybody, but at me especially. "Come on, Morrison," he would bellow during parade-ground marches, "this is no bleedin' tea party. Get in STEP!" During inspections, he always found something wrong with my kit, or uniform or rifle, and I can still smell his foul smoker's breath as he ranted in my face, his eyes blazing above his blotchy red nose and ratty little moustache.

"You think this is all *funny*, Private? You think you're too good for this? I'll wipe that *superior* look off your face!"

I couldn't count the number of times I'd had the word "su-*peee*-ria" (as he pronounced it) spat out at me. Sometimes shreds of tobacco from his hand-rolled cigarettes would land on my face. I don't know why he singled me out so often. I wasn't the worst soldier in the platoon. There was one chubby Italian named Pullio who was always out of breath. And there were a couple of Polish boys who could barely understand English.

But I wasn't a natural soldier like Mackie, that's for sure. Kewley had picked him as one of his favourites right away. When I crawled outside the tent in my shorts, I saw Mackie happily stretching his muscles in the sunshine. The barrel-chested PT instructor soon arrived and blew his whistle and we formed into lines. We started with jumping jacks, then knee bends with arms straight out, then push-ups followed by running in place. For athletes like Mackie, this was easy. I'd always avoided sports and had hated PT classes in high school. After doing twenty morning push-ups my arms would get rubbery and I'd flop down on the grass. Luckily, the PT instructor didn't seem to notice.

After PT, we'd grab our towels and head to the wash house for a cold shower and shave. The smell of frying bacon from the mess hall made us all hungry. Everyone liked to complain about the army chow, but for most of the recruits it was better food than they were used to at home. In the chow line I'd see plates piled high with scrambled eggs and bacon and sometimes we even had sausages. Boots clumped on the bare floorboards of the newly built mess hall, which still had tarpaper on the outside walls. Giant barracks buildings were under construction, but they wouldn't be ready before our twelve-week training period was finished. So it would be old Bell tents left over from the 1914–18 war for us. Our khaki uniforms, steel helmets and Lee-Enfield rifles were all Great War holdovers, too. So were the big clumsy gas masks we carried in our kit bags.

At least we didn't have to dig trenches like most of the Royals had done during their training at Camp Borden only a few months before. We could still see the trenches in a nearby field, now half-filled with rainwater. I thought of my dad having to live in a trench like that during the last war.

The first group of soldiers from the Royal Regiment had shipped out for England in June. But they had ended up in Iceland instead. Hitler's forces had invaded Denmark and Norway on April 9, 1940, and it was feared that Iceland might be next. The Royals were now encamped near Reykjavik and we expected to be joining them there in a few months.

But by August everyone knew that this war would

be more about airplanes than trenches. Truckloads of trainee pilots for the Royal Canadian Air Force were arriving at Borden every day. On training flights, some of them liked to swoop down over us and waggle their wings. Mackie would look up and say, "Allie, we should have joined the Air Force."

"Sure, if you want to get yourself killed in a hurry," was my usual response. In the skies over England, British pilots in their Spitfires were already engaged in fierce combat with the Messerschmitts of Hitler's Luftwaffe. At the end of June we had seen newsreels of Hitler strutting about Paris as if he owned it — which, in fact, he did. After the fall of France, we heard British Prime Minister Winston Churchill's unforgettable speech on the radio:

> . . . the Battle of France is over. I expect that the Battle of Britain is about to begin. . . . The whole fury and might of the enemy must very soon be turned on us. . . . Let us therefore brace ourselves to our duties, and so bear ourselves, that, if the British Empire and its Commonwealth last for a thousand years, men will still say, 'This was their finest hour.'

Soon the radio news gave reports of the bombing raids in London and other British cities. My mother had written to me that she was worried about Aunt Lil and her relatives in Glasgow. With Britain facing possible Nazi invasion, all the training at Camp Borden picked up speed. Maybe it was the thought of Hitler's troops marching into his dear old London that made Kewley so fierce with us.

Our training sessions began right after breakfast. Rifle practice was not *my* finest hour. My shots always seemed to land in the hay bales rather than on the paper targets attached to them. Mackie's targets usually sported a few bullseyes. He had also quickly mastered field-stripping his Lee-Enfield rifle, taking out the bolt and other parts, laying them out and then putting them back together again. Kewley had announced that we would soon have to do this blindfolded. I could barely manage it with my eyes open.

Bayonet practice was another round of misery for me. Once we had fitted the long, nasty bayonet spikes to the barrels of our rifles, we were supposed to charge at hanging sacks of hay and shove our bayonets into them, yelling loudly all the while. On our first charge I collided with Pullio and we both fell to the ground laughing. In a flash Kewley's bulldog face was over mine.

"So, Private, this is all so amusing for you, so funny! 'Ow funny will it be when a Nazi attacks your sister, EH? Answer me that!"

"Not funny, sir," I mumbled.

"*Louder*, Private!" Kewley bellowed.

"Not funny, *sir!*" I yelled, now standing rigidly at attention.

I didn't find the idea of jamming a bayonet into another man's stomach particularly funny, either, even if he was a Nazi. One thing I *was* able to master was a pretty good imitation of Kewley bellowing, "'Owd you loike it if a *Narr-zi* attacked your *sistah?*" for the off-hours amusement of Mackie and some of the others. Whenever we heard a lousy joke, Mackie and I would say in unison, "Not funny, *sir!*" which used to crack people up.

And yet I think Mackie was a little embarrassed that I was seen as the biggest screw-up in the platoon. He had started to hang out with some of the guys who had been "Saturday soldiers" in the militia. Basic training was a piece of cake for them. A few would likely gain a chevron stripe for their shoulders and become lance-corporals when we joined the rest of the regiment. I wondered if maybe Mackie had his eye on getting a stripe, but he only laughed when I asked him.

He did help me to practise field-stripping a rifle, though. When I wasn't nervous about doing it in front of Kewley, I could manage it fine. And Mackie was a patient teacher. But he couldn't help me on the parade ground, when I would get out of step or be slow to snap my rifle into position when Kewley bellowed out, "Pre-sent *arms!*" Kewley thought I was doing this on purpose but I wasn't. I just got easily flustered around him.

Parade happened just before they gave us lunch — which typically consisted of soup, baloney sandwiches and tea. After lunch we went on route marches. The Royals were an infantry regiment and we soon learned what being a "foot soldier" really meant. On Mondays we would have a 5-mile route march; on Tuesdays it would be 10 miles. The length would increase by 5 miles each day until Friday's big 25-mile slog. Some of these were light-pack marches and some were full-pack. On full-pack marches we wore our steel helmets, khaki uniforms and all our "webbing" — the cloth twill belts that held our front pack, including a gas mask, and our backpack, which held a rain poncho, socks, underwear and another pair of boots.

It was usually younger training officers who accompanied us on the route marches rather than Kewley, which was a relief to me. And on the hotter days, they usually allowed us to have light-pack marches with just our backpacks and water bottles.

During the first week of route marches, my new boots gave me blisters the size of grapes. Every hour we would stop for ten minutes of rest and foot inspection. We would have to take off our boots, dry our feet, puncture and bandage our blisters, use foot powder, and change our socks or even boots if necessary. Both pairs of boots gave me blisters and during the first week I was limping a lot. But my feet soon toughened up and I began to actually like the route marches. They got me out of camp, away from Kewley, and I enjoyed tramping along country roads in the summer sunshine. Sometimes we would sing army marching songs, many with words too filthy to repeat, like the famous one about Hitler having only one part to his anatomy where most men have two. . . .

And since we were Royals we learned the unofficial Royal Regiment song. The nickname for the Royals was "Basher's Dashers," after Lt-Colonel G. Hedley Basher, the Royals' Commanding Officer, who was then with the regiment in Iceland. I can still remember the words:

We had to join UP, We had to join UP!
We had to join old Basher's Dashers.
Two bucks a week
Bugger all to eat
Great big boots and blisters on our feet.

We'd then repeat the "join *up*" chorus until the last verse:

> *If it wasn't for the war*
> *We'd have buggered off before.*
> *Basher, you're balmy!*

* * *

By late September, we had moved on to more advanced training. I discovered that I wasn't bad at map reading and using a compass. At the gunnery range we were given Tommy guns to teach us about automatic weapons. We'd seen these Thompson submachine guns in gangster movies like *Scarface*, and using them made us feel like Chicago mobsters. "Gotcha, you dirty rat," I yelled in my best James Cagney voice whenever I hit the target.

Mackie and some of the militia boys also received training on Bren guns, a newer, lighter machine gun. Mackie and the others would lie on their bellies to fire them after flipping down the small bipod legs that held up the barrel.

As the leaves on the trees around the camp started turning yellow, I began to feel more and more like a soldier. I could now get through PT training without collapsing on the grass each morning. I'd noticed some bumps emerging on the backs of my arms that Mackie told me were tricep muscles. Even Pullio, I noticed, had lost some of the jowls around his chin. I considered him a friend now. All the men in the platoon had bonded from the sweating and suffering we'd done in training together. Having grown up in a mostly female household, I enjoyed feeling like a man among men.

We were also united by our hatred of Kewley. To our relief, we had seen less of him recently. Then one afternoon he showed up to tell us he would be leading us on a route march. But this time, he said, it would be a tactical patrol. We all groaned when he told us to get into full battle dress and bring our rifles. When we had regrouped, he told us to pull out our boot polish and blacken our faces. Then he led us off in quick time, shouting orders as we went.

We left the gates of the camp and headed out onto country roads. He made us march in step most of the time. Nobody felt like singing. After we were about 10 miles away from Borden he turned us around. Soon we came to a logging road off to our left and he marched us onto that. Before long, we found ourselves slogging through deep woods. The logging road narrowed down to a trail and we soon approached a limestone cliff which we had to scale hand over hand. Several hills followed, which Kewley made us run up and down until we came to a river that we had to ford holding our rifles over our heads.

The sun was getting lower in the sky and still we pushed on into the woods. By now there was no trail at all that anyone could see. I couldn't tell if we were on army land or not. Camp Borden covered 20,000 acres and much of it was bush. As we pushed onwards into a cedar swamp, many of us became convinced that Kewley was lost. We were all tired, wet and miserable, and afraid of missing our supper. We should have been heading west to get back to the camp, but Kewley was leading us to the northeast. I screwed up my courage and approached him.

"Sir, to get back to camp, shouldn't we be heading that way?" I asked, pointing west.

"Did I ask for your advice, Private?" he roared, his red face turning purplish.

"No, sir."

"Then keep your trap *shut!* All right men," he called out, "follow me!"

We all groaned as he started crashing through the bush up the next hill and down the other side. I was now not far behind him and we stopped at the bottom beside an algae-covered pond to wait for the other men. Suddenly Pullio, with some others behind him, came crashing down the hill and slammed into me — pushing me right into the green slime of the pond. I stood up spitting water and swearing at Pullio. But within a few seconds it actually felt cool and refreshing. I scooped up a handful of mud and threw it at him. He threw some back. I threw some more and hit Murphy, a short guy who loved a good scrap, and in a few minutes a mud fight was in full swing.

Kewley had walked on ahead but came racing back. He immediately started ranting at me. I dragged myself out of the pond and lay panting on the bank, trying to scrape the mud off my legs and boots. Kewley was raging and waving his cane as he stood over me, calling me every foul name in the book. Suddenly Mackie was behind him. He took Kewley by the shoulders and moved him aside.

"Enough," he said firmly. "That's enough." Then he reached down and helped me up and handed me my rifle.

Kewley erupted. "That's a serious *offense!*" he spluttered. "Striking a superior, that's a *court martial*. You're *finished* boy, you're *finished*. It'll be the stockade for you, for a long, *long* time!"

For the rest of the walk back I was in a daze.

We came out of the woods and saw tank tread marks in a field, which indicated that we weren't far from camp. After supper (which I could barely eat) the military police came for Mackie and me. The "meatheads" took us to the headquarters building. Mackie was taken into one room and they motioned me into another. Two officers were sitting in chairs when I entered the room. I saluted and was told to stand at ease. They then asked me to describe what had happened. I talked while they made notes. When I was finished, they asked a few questions and I was told to wait outside. I felt sick. I didn't care if they threw me out — it was all my fault. But Mackie didn't deserve to be court-martialled and thrown in a military prison. Eventually, Mackie came out and we were both dismissed. As we walked back to our tents I asked him if we were going to be thrown out.

"Na-a-aw," he said. "Are you kidding? They know Kewley's a horse's ass."

"So what's gonna happen?" I asked.

"Oh, confined to barracks, dock our pay, full-pack drill, stuff like that."

I wasn't sure I believed him, but I hoped he was right. And it helped me to get to sleep that night.

The next morning, Mackie and I were called before three officers. We were given a stern lecture about how serious the charges against us were. We were told that they would go down permanently on our army record and that we would be docked two weeks' pay.

"Ordinarily," the major concluded, "I'd have you two walking the parade ground till after midnight, with no leave till Christmas. However," he continued, "we're at war, so things are a little different."

We were then told that our training period was finishing early and we were being shipped off to England. The Royal Regiment was leaving Iceland to help in the defence of Britain. We would join them there. Tomorrow we would begin four days' leave. After that we would go to Halifax to sail for England.

After we were dismissed and out of earshot, Mackie yelped and grabbed me in a headlock, rubbing his fist in my hair. "Saved by the bell, Allie, saved by the bleedin' bell!" Then he added, in a mock-English accent. "Gor' blimey we're off to Blighty." At this we both laughed like maniacs, completely giddy with relief.

The next day we rode the train down to Toronto together. As Mackie looked out the window, he turned to me and said, "Well, did you hear that ol' Kewley ended up face down in Crap Creek last night?"

"You're kidding!" I replied, imagining Kewley's face covered in muck from the camp's smelly drainage ditch. "Did he fall in? Was he drunk?"

"Yes," said Mackie with grin, "but let's just say he had a little *help* getting there." My eyes widened but Mackie then held up his hands to indicate "no further questions."

I nodded and put my head back against the seat. Outside, the brilliant reds and golds of the farmers' woodlots began to give way to small towns on the outskirts of Toronto. I remembered the last thing the major had said to us: "We're at war, so things are a little different."

They sure are, I thought to myself. They sure are.

CHAPTER 3
ON BOARD THE *EMPRESS*
November 10, 1940

Mackie was sitting sideways in his hammock holding a hand of cards, when the ship suddenly lurched. All the hammocks in the tiny, smoke-filled cabin swung back and forth, but the card game continued.

"Hard to believe this tub had the king and queen on it last year," I remarked after the swaying stopped. The card players ignored me. Then Murphy, who wasn't in the card game, crawled out of his hammock.

"Gonna do like the king," he said, opening the door to the cabin, "and go sit on the throne."

"Be sure you do a royal flush," said Mackie with a grin. "Because, gents," he continued, slapping his cards down, "that's what *I* have."

A loud groan erupted at Mackie's winning hand as the ship lurched again, sending cards, dollar bills and packs of cigarettes flying.

The *Empress of Australia* was doing a zigzag course across the North Atlantic to avoid German submarines. The liner had been stripped of all her carved panelling, comfortable chairs and rich carpeting before we boarded in Halifax. Now painted a dull grey, she didn't look much like the elegant ship that had brought King George VI and Queen Elizabeth to Canada for their 1939 royal tour.

On the upper decks, anti-aircraft guns pointed skyward. A troopship with over four thousand men crammed into it would have made a great target. When we were assigned to the tiny cabins down on D-deck, my first thought was that if a torpedo from a German U-boat ever struck us we'd be trapped like rats. But we soon discovered that there were some advantages. When we hit rough weather on our first day out, those of us lower down in the ship were much less seasick than the men higher up. The former grand dining saloon on A-deck was hung with hundreds of hammocks, and there almost everybody was nauseous and vomiting. The smell in that room was enough to make your guts churn.

By the third day the weather had calmed and regular army routine resumed. We started every day with PT exercises on deck. And we had a full schedule of daily inspections, stripping and cleaning of weapons, and drills. The army was determined to keep us in fighting shape. But the officers were a little more lenient than usual and there were no Kewley types on board, luckily. In addition to our platoon from the Royal Regiment, there were men from the Essex Scottish of Windsor, Ontario, the South Saskatchewan Regiment and the Fusiliers Mont-Royal from Montreal. We would all be stationed together in England as part of the 2nd Canadian Division. I tried out my high-school French with a couple of the Fusiliers and usually got an answer back in English.

Mackie's cabin was the preferred hangout spot for the Royals on D-deck. He was the most popular guy in the platoon. I didn't play cards or smoke, so when I dropped in there, I sometimes felt like his annoying kid brother. I was glad that nobody smoked in my cabin, which I shared with five others including Pullio. Remembering the smell of Kewley's tobacco breath was enough to put me off cigarettes for life — one of the few things I can thank him for.

When the ship was lurching, I found that lying in my hammock was the best place to be. I was happy to spend my off-hours there reading the paperback books I'd picked up in a second-hand store during my final leave at home. I'd even found an old travel guide to London and was marking off the places I most wanted to visit. I only hoped Hitler's bombs wouldn't destroy Westminster Abbey or the Tower of London before I could see them.

On our sixth morning, I looked through our tiny

porthole and saw land in the distance. During PT exercises on deck, green hills topped with heavy grey clouds came into view. The ship's bow was pointed towards what looked like the mouth of a large river. Before long I spotted the grey stone buildings and church spires of a seaside town. It reminded me of Largs, a place we'd gone to for holidays when I was a small boy. Steamer excursions from Glasgow went down the River Clyde in summer — people called it "goin' doon the watter" in Glaswegian slang.

After PT was finished I said to Mackie, "Those hills remind me of Scotland. We might be going up the Clyde."

"You think so?" he said. "I'll find out."

He went off and chatted to one of the ship's crewmen — Mackie knew everybody on board, it seemed — and then came back.

"Yup, it's the Clyde," he said. "We're supposed to land in a place called Goo-rock."

"Gourock, right," I said, pronouncing it correctly. "It's near Greenock, just down the Clyde from Glasgow."

"Well, Allie," said Mackie, throwing his arm around my shoulder. "The two Scotsmen are going home!"

"Aye, aye!" I replied, sensing his excitement. I looked forward to writing to my mother about being back in Scotland.

As we walked down the gangplank in Gourock, some of the local women had hot tea and sandwiches waiting for us. I told a couple of them that I'd been born and raised in Glasgow. "You sound a right Canadian now, son," one woman said, "you've lost your accent."

We then marched to the train station and boarded the train for Glasgow, from which we took another train south. People stood in the windows of houses along the railway tracks and waved white pillowcases to welcome us. Although it was a grey November day, the Scottish countryside was green and "awfa bonnie," as my mother might say. Mackie kept pointing at all the ruined castles — becoming quite the proud Scot, all of a sudden.

We didn't get to Aldershot till the wee hours of the morning, and then we were marched quietly through the town to one of the huge red-brick barracks that could hold a whole company.

Mandora Barracks
Aldershot, England
November 15, 1940

Dear Mum:

Just a note to let you know that we're now in Aldershot, England, after taking the train down from Scotland. (We sailed right past Largs where we used to go on holidays!) Aldershot has been a big army camp since Queen Victoria's day. The barracks are barely heated and we are all freezing! Every morning for inspection we must fold the blankets on our bunks in a special way with a second blanket tied around it. On top of that we have to put out our boots with the soles facing upwards so they can check that the hobnails are clean and shiny. Over here the army sure has its own way of doing things!

We're less than an hour by train from London, so I'm looking forward to seeing the sights when I get some leave. But don't worry, I won't go there when the bombs are falling! I hope to get up to Glasgow, too, when I can get a seven-day pass, and will write to Aunt Lil to let the relatives know I'm coming. If you see Mackie's mum, you can let her know that he's doing fine. (I don't think he's the world's best letter writer.)

Much love to you and to Elspeth and Doreen. Tell Elspeth I haven't found her a boyfriend yet. She wouldn't want an English one — they all have scary bad teeth!

Yours,

Alistair

CHAPTER 4

LONDON PRIDE
November 28, 1940

"Come on, Allie, run for it! Run, run, *run!*"

Mackie was hollering from the window of the train as I sprinted down the platform. The conductor blew his whistle and the train began to move, so I ran even faster. When I finally reached Mackie, he opened the door and pulled me in and I fell panting into a seat beside him. Murphy grabbed my bag and tossed it into the netting of the overhead rack.

"Fartley kept me right to the last minute," I gasped between heaving breaths. Fartley was our name for Sergeant Hartley. He wasn't a bad guy, really, just a stickler for the rules. And it wasn't his fault I'd made a sloppy showing at inspection that morning. I'd stayed up reading with a flashlight the night before, paging through my London guidebook to choose all the places I most wanted to see. I'd awoken in a groggy state and hadn't made the folds on my blankets exactly knife-sharp. My boots, too, could have used a little more spit and polish.

"Sergeant, make sure this man is given extra duty!" Lieutenant Whitman had called out during inspection after breakfast. (Whitman was from Toronto but he had studied at Cambridge University, where he'd picked up a phony English accent that earned him the nickname Twitman from us.)

Extra duty on our first two-day leave! I could have kicked myself. Sergeant Hartley set me to work polishing the brass doorknobs in the barracks. Mackie and Murphy were getting impatient waiting for me, so I told them I'd meet them at the station for the 10:15 train.

After they left, Fartley told me I had to clean out the ashes from the coal-burning grates that barely heated the barracks. This filthy job took most of an hour, so when I was finally dismissed I had to wash up and make a mad dash through the town to the train station.

As I settled into the seat and my breathing calmed down, the train picked up speed. We could see into the windows of the houses and tenements close to the railway tracks. Some still had their blackout curtains drawn. Every home in Britain was required to have long, black curtains to shut out any light that might help the Luftwaffe find their targets during night bombing raids. Since Hitler's Blitz had begun in early September, bombs had been dropping on London almost every night. Aldershot was only 40 miles from London and we could sometimes hear the distant *crump-crump* sound of the bombs and the rapid *ack-ack* of the anti-aircraft guns.

As the train came closer to central London we began to see bomb damage. It was eerie to look into apartment blocks that had been half blown away and see rooms with flowered wallpaper and pictures still on the walls. The train suddenly went into a long, dark tunnel and within a few minutes we were beside the platform at Waterloo Station. We piled out of the train and pushed our way through the crowds in the concourse to the main entrance.

"Let's walk to Trafalgar Square — it's not that far," I said.

Following the map from my guidebook, we took a bridge across the River Thames. I pointed out the Houses of Parliament downriver. The sun broke through the November clouds as we walked into Trafalgar Square — which was swarming with pigeons! Before I knew it we were posing for tintype photographs with pigeons sitting on our arms. Just like typical tourists! Oh well, I thought, I can always send my photo home to my mother and sisters. I suggested we walk up the steps of the National Gallery that faces onto the square. From the portico we had a perfect view of Nelson's Column, a tall granite monument with a statue of Admiral Nelson on top. The great naval hero of the Napoleonic wars looked down on a city that was once again at war. In the sky behind him floated cigar-shaped barrage balloons, designed to deflect low-flying enemy planes. *Buy National War Bonds* had been painted on the base of the monument, and the square's famous fountains had been turned off. To three young men from the colonies, however, this was the grandest sight we had ever seen. Here we were at the heart of the British Empire, at the centre of the world, or so it seemed to us. We stood there quietly for a few minutes.

"Piccadilly. How about we check out Piccadilly?" Murphy said, breaking the silence. "That's where the girls are supposed to be."

"We can always do that later, Murph" I said. "Don't you want to see Buckingham Palace?"

Grudgingly Murphy tagged along as we walked across Trafalgar Square and through the gates of Admiralty Arch onto a wide boulevard called The Mall. I remembered seeing newspaper photos of crowds lining this grand avenue to see the king and queen in their golden coach during the coronation procession in May of 1937. My mother had taken us to the cinema to see a film about the coronation. ("The queen is Scots, you know," she had told me more than once.) It seemed hard to believe that a German plane had recently flown right up the Mall and bombed Buckingham Palace, destroying the chapel.

As we approached the palace we saw the giant monument to Queen Victoria in front of it. I pointed out the royal standard flapping on the flagpole, and explained that it indicated that the king was in residence. The king and queen had chosen to stay in London despite the bombing and this had won them special affection from Londoners. Sandbags surrounded the palace's wrought-iron gates and there were lots of jeeps and soldiers nearby. We peered through the railings and I pointed out the balcony where the royal family often stood to wave to the crowds.

"Doesn't look like they're gonna ask us in for tea," groused Murphy after we'd stared at the windows for a while. "How far is it to Piccadilly from here?'

"The pubs are closed now, Murph," I said a little impatiently. "We can always go there later. You have to tell your mum you saw Big Ben."

Mackie followed me with Murphy behind as we walked down a street called Birdcage Walk. It ran beside St. James's Park and we could see the tower of Big Ben and the spires of the Houses of Parliament through the bare trees of the elegant park. When we finally approached the Parliament Buildings, we saw that high rows of sandbags with rolls of barbed wire on top surrounded them. But they still were very grand and impressive to us. We stood and waited to hear Big Ben chime and it sounded just the way it did before the noon news on CBC radio. The Germans had tried to bomb Big Ben and its tower was a little scarred, but the huge clock still kept perfect time.

We then went on to Westminster Abbey right next door. This ancient building had been bombed recently as well, but luckily only the courtyard had been damaged. I spied some of the memorial plaques to famous people on the walls and began reading them. But I soon sensed that Mackie and Murphy were getting bored. Murphy had a so-what-am-I-doing-in-this-old-church? expression on his round face. I took them to the chapel that held the tomb of Queen Elizabeth I, but even the great old Tudor queen lying there carved in marble, holding her orb and sceptre, did not impress them.

"Well, maybe the Coronation Chair . . . " I began to say but Mackie interrupted.

"Uh, Allie," he said, "Murph and I were just thinking — "

"It's okay," I said. "I know you guys have had it. Well, I can always come back . . . "

"No, no," said Mackie. "You stay. You like this stuff. We'll catch up with you later. We'll be at the Hammersmith Palais tonight. We can meet up there."

"Oh, sure, sure, that's fine," I said as they made a hasty beeline for the door. The Palais was a big dance hall that all the soldiers talked about. I figured I could get there on the Tube, the London subway system. I felt a little let down that Mack and Murph wanted to go off without me. But then I thought, Well, okay, maybe this is better, now I can explore London on my own.

I asked a guard where I'd find the Coronation Chair.

"Oh no, son, that's been taken away for safe-keeping," he replied. "Bombs, you know. And we can't let Jerry 'ave it."

To think of the chair in which England's monarchs had been crowned for over six hundred years being destroyed — or taken off to Germany after an invasion — that was shocking, even to a Scot. Under the seat of the Coronation Chair lay the famous Stone of Scone, on which Scotland's ancient kings had once been crowned. King Edward I had brought the stone to England in 1297 to show that he had conquered the Scots. And the Scots had resented it ever since. I remembered my father reading to me about William Wallace and Robert the Bruce and all the great kings of Scotland. I'd wanted to touch the legendary Stone of Destiny, as it was called, for my dad's sake. Perhaps I'd inherited my love of history from him.

Oh well, there was still the Tower of London to see.

* * *

"If you've come to see the jewels, Canada, they're not 'ere," said a young soldier with a friendly face and a strong Cockney accent.

"Beg pardon?" I said, finding him hard to follow.

"The Crown jewels — they've taken 'em away. I think *you* 'ave 'em, or so I've 'eard," he replied, nodding at the *Canada* patch on my arm.

So Britain's fabulous crown jewels had been taken from the Tower of London to be hidden from Hitler. Could they actually have taken them to Canada? I wondered. Clearly, the Brits really believed that the Nazis might be about to invade.

"Oh, okay," I said to the soldier. "But can I have a look at the Tower?"

"Can't go inside. But come on, I'll show you round. I'm off duty for a bit," he said, opening the heavy wooden gate.

Alf, as the Cockney soldier was called, told me he was with the Royal Fusiliers who were stationed in the Tower's Waterloo Barracks. In a few minutes we were inside the outer walls and standing beside a massive stone fortress with four turrets.

"That's the White Tower," said Alf. "Lots of famous people were locked up in there."

I looked up at the tiny windows and thought of Queen Anne Boleyn taking a last look out before her beheading on a May morning in 1536. As if reading my thoughts, Alf pointed to the battlements and said, "They say the ghost of Anne Boleyn walks up 'ere some nights. I can show you where she got the chop, if you like."

We walked around to Tower Green, where so many people had died on the scaffold. There was a huge black raven sitting on a post. Alf told me his name was Grip and that he was the last of the famous ravens who had always lived at the Tower. The others had all died since the bombing began.

"We 'ave to take good care of ol' Grip 'ere," said Alf. "'Cos it's believed that so long as the ravens remain at the Tower of London, England is safe from invasion."

"Gee, I hope Hitler doesn't know you're down to your last raven," I joked, but Alf looked at me unsmilingly.

"Bloody Jerries. We might 'ave a visit from 'em tonight with those clouds clearin'," he said as he looked up at the sun that was heading towards the horizon.

On my way out we walked along the river side of the Tower so I could see Traitor's Gate, once the much-feared entrance for prisoners arriving by boat. I thought of the young Princess Elizabeth being taken there in 1554 on the orders of her sister, the queen remembered as Bloody Mary. Elizabeth had thought that she would face the same fate as her mother, Anne Boleyn, but instead she was released after eight weeks, then proclaimed queen when Mary died four years later. I thought back to the marble effigy of Queen Elizabeth I that I'd seen only hours ago in Westminster Abbey.

* * *

After saying thanks and goodbye to Alf, I walked across the Thames on the castle-like Tower Bridge and saw a brilliant sunset from there. On the other side of the river I ate some beans on toast and a jam tart with a cup of tea at a workman's café. (A lot of the Canadians complained about English food, but I didn't mind it. It reminded me of my mother's cooking.)

After supper, I crossed back over the Thames on London Bridge, humming the famous nursery song about it falling down, falling down. I wondered to myself if that song was known in Germany and whether the Luftwaffe might be planning to make it come true.

I had thought I might take the Tube out to Hammersmith to meet up with Mackie and Murph at the Palais dance hall. But when the sirens began sounding, I realized the Tube would likely be shut down — the Underground stations became shelters during air raids.

People started streaming towards one.

"Come on, Canada!" a woman in a headscarf called out to me. "Best 'urry on down to shelter."

I followed her to the station entrance and joined the others descending the stairs below a red poster that said *Your Courage, Your Cheerfulness, Your Resolution WILL BRING VICTORY.* But that advice didn't seem necessary for this station. All along the platform people were cheerfully sitting or lying on blankets and chatting to each other as if it were a friendly neighbourhood gathering place. Down at one end, two boys were playing harmonicas and a few people were singing and clapping along with them.

I crouched down near a pillar next to a woman with her hair tied up in a bandanna. She had three young children lying beside her under a blanket.

"Everyone seems very calm down here," I said to her.

"We've 'ad practice," she replied. "Since the bleedin' Blitz started, we've been down 'ere every bloomin' night, seems like. Our kiddies were evacuated to the country last year but they missed their mum and I missed them. So I brought 'em back home and then Hitler starts all this bleedin' nonsense. Least we 'aven't been bombed out yet, so we're luckier than some."

She offered me tea from a thermos, and a biscuit, both of which I accepted. As we chatted, I learned that her husband was in the Royal Navy. She hadn't told him the children were back with her in London, as she didn't want to worry him. "He's got enough worries — what with the U-boats and all."

I mentioned that German submarines hadn't troubled us on our trip over from Halifax last month. She said that her husband had been to Halifax more than once. His destroyer was part of a convoy that guarded ships bringing supplies to Britain across the North Atlantic. When I said

I was from Canada, an old woman lying nearby decided to join our chat. She had a cousin in Winnipeg, she announced. The family's name was Smedley. Perhaps I knew them? I smiled and explained that Winnipeg was a long way from Toronto. Every English person, it seemed, had a relative in Canada.

The harmonica players down at the far end now had a fair-sized group around them, and snatches of rollicking old songs kept drifting our way. It occurred to me that if Hitler really believed the bombing would destroy the morale of the British, he'd better think again.

Suddenly we heard the sirens wailing once more. This was followed by thudding explosions. The singing stopped. One bomb must have fallen nearby, since the whole platform shuddered. My neighbour in the bandanna put her arms around her children and drew them close. The old lady said, "They must be aiming for St. Paul's again."

I knew that St. Paul's Cathedral had been a frequent target for the Luftwaffe. And although it had been damaged a little, its great white dome still stood as a symbol of defiance for Londoners. I'd seen it while crossing London Bridge, so realized it couldn't be far away.

I suddenly wondered if I shouldn't be up top

helping. They hadn't told us what to do if we were caught in an air raid. But I was a soldier after all. If Mackie were here, he'd want to do something.

As I stood up and headed towards the stairs, the woman in the bandanna called out to me, "You mustn't go, Canada! They 'aven't sounded the All Clear yet!"

I turned and gave her a little salute and then sprinted up the stairs.

It was pitch black on the street. And it smelled of gas and heavy smoke. Looking up, I could see searchlights raking the sky, illuminating barrage balloons. Then, above the rooftops I saw flames licking upwards through billowing smoke. As I walked in the direction of the fire, the air thickened and glowing cinders and ashes blew past my face. Turning a corner I suddenly saw a whole block of shops in flames. On the street a double-decker bus was already a blackened shell. I hoped that it had been empty when the bombs hit. Firemen were already on the scene, the water from their hoses illuminated by the light of the flames. But one fire engine wasn't enough to fight this fire.

Then I saw an older man with an air-raid warden's badge on his black overcoat. He was wearing a steel helmet and passing out buckets to some teenaged boys. I went over and asked if I could help.

"You can join this bucket brigade if you like," he said, passing me a tin bucket.

Some of the boys had run down to the river and were passing up water in buckets. At first each boy had to run several yards with his bucket, but before long more people joined us and we were able to simply pass buckets on to the person next to us. It seemed crazy to be fighting a huge fire with only buckets, but at least we were doing something. Another fire engine arrived just as a large roof collapsed, sending up a huge cloud of flames and fiery debris. The air-raid warden shouted and waved us back from the area. We retreated for a much-needed breather and, after a while, the bucket brigade began again.

As the sky lightened, the fire died a little and the firemen began hosing down smouldering beams that had fallen inside the stone walls. A truck arrived with some water tanks and the air-raid warden bailed out water from a dipper to his volunteers. I gratefully drank from the dipper when it was passed.

A breeze stirred a swirl of charred embers from the pavement. I was shocked to realize they were pages from books.

"These were bookshops," said the air-raid warden, "and had been for hundreds of years."

I kicked a blackened pile of ashes to reveal some books that were still intact. Bending down, I pulled out a leather-bound one that still had shiny gold trim on its pages. It was *Rob Roy* by Sir Walter Scott, one of my father's favourites. I buttoned it into the largest pocket of my jacket.

I then turned and saw the great dome of St. Paul's Cathedral still standing in the dawn light. My chest was filled with smoke and my face and uniform were black. But I felt very calm and strangely happy.

I knew that this had been one of the most unforgettable nights of my life.

CHAPTER 5

ON THE SOUTH COAST

December 5, 1940

Dear Mum:

I made it to London!

Enclosed is a picture of Mackie and me in Trafalgar Square, all covered in pigeons — just like that photo of you and Dad on your honeymoon. Even with a war on, the photographers there still manage to soak the tourists!

It was a thrill to see all the famous spots like Westminster Abbey and Buckingham Palace — even with sandbags around them. (The queen was home but didn't ask us in for tea . . .) I couldn't get into the Tower of London but a pleasant English fellow showed me around the outside of it.

London "carries on," as you've no doubt heard on the radio. The Blitz has only made the English more determined. And London is still the grandest city I've ever seen.

This is only a brief note, as they're shipping us out somewhere. Even if I knew where, I couldn't tell you. The military censor would only black it out of this letter, anyway.

But you needn't worry about me, I don't think Jerry's about to invade. All the action we've had so far is just drills, drills and more drills.

Love to Elspeth and Doreen,

Alistair

I didn't tell my mother about the air raid — it would only have upset her. And I didn't tell Mackie and Murph much about what had happened to me, either. They only wanted to talk about the girls they had met at the Hammersmith Palais. (Mackie, I knew, did a mean jitterbug, and apparently the girls were lining up to be tossed around the dance floor by him.)

Sergeant Hartley wasn't impressed with my smoke-blackened uniform and boots, or my story of how they got that way.

"Doing a little night fighting on leave, were you, Morrison?" he said when I told him about the air raid. "No medals for that, my boy."

His sarcasm kept me from telling anyone about my Blitz experience for a long, long time. I washed my blackened khakis in a washtub and pressed them by laying the pants and jacket under my mattress. But the uniform smelled of smoke for months afterwards. Fortunately I had a second uniform, so I was able to wear that for inspection.

I wrote the letter to my mother in a train car crammed with soldiers heading for England's south coast. Our destination turned out to be a town called Lewes — I said it once and a local told me straight off that it was pronounced "Lewis" — which is only a few miles inland from the more famous seaside town of Brighton. Glowering over Lewes is a hulking stone castle that was built by William the Conquerer eight centuries before. Looking up at its high walls, I imagined the defenders inside pouring boiling oil down on their attackers. But the castle wouldn't be of much use in a battle with tanks and bombers, the kind of invasion we were expecting might come any day.

Our battalion spent four months in Lewes, a time we all called "waiting for Jerry." Yet all they had us doing was marching, marching, marching, and keeping fit and rifle drills. Sometimes we took part in war games called "manoeuvres" with other battalions. Once we had to play the part of the Jerries in a mock attack against the British Home Guard, a volunteer group of civilian Brits.

These (mostly elderly) English gents armed with wooden rifles and broom handles took it all very seriously, though.

In Lewes we stayed in the old town hall and slept on big burlap bags filled with straw called "palliasses." At Christmas, the Red Cross and some women in the town put on the best English Christmas dinner they could make for us, given wartime rationing. (The rum in the plum pudding seemed to be real, though likely it wasn't.) But Hitler chose to play Scrooge by using the holiday season as a time to step up the Blitz. The Luftwaffe pounded London in heavy night bombing raids right through New Year's. They kept trying to hit St. Paul's Cathedral, but I heard on the radio that its white dome still stood intact. I thought of the navy wife and her three children that I'd met huddled in the nearby Tube station, and hoped they were all right. At night we could hear the steady drone of Luftwaffe bombers passing overhead. Sometimes on our route marches we would see a downed German bomber lying in a field. Occasionally we'd see a crashed RAF Spitfire and hope that the pilot had bailed out in time.

There wasn't much snow during our first English winter, but the daily freezing drizzle made it seem colder than any winter in Canada. I did like it when snowdrops and crocuses began popping out of the ground in the gardens during January and February, though — much earlier than I ever saw them in Ontario.

In April we were transferred to Winchelsea, a town near the seacoast. There we slept in wooden cottages on the beachfront and really shivered when the raw April winds blew in off the English Channel. During daily exercises we dug slit trenches, laid minefields and practised manning our defences.

But still we had our endless route marches along the coastal roads. I noticed Mackie casting envious looks at the soldiers who roared by us on English-made Norton motorcycles that were painted a military green. One morning after parade, Lieutenant Whitman made an announcement. "Any man here who has experience riding a motorcycle, step forward!"

Mackie instantly took a huge step forward, placing himself right under Twitman's nose.

What the heck is he doing? I wondered. Mackie had never ridden anything faster than his grocery-delivery bicycle! He and a couple of other volunteers marched off behind Twitman. When I saw him at lunch that day he was very excited. "I'm gonna be a dispatch rider," he told me, grasping imaginary handlebars and making a revving-up noise. "Running messages to Hastings, Brighton, all over the place."

"Mackie!" I said in a low voice. "What happens when they find out you don't know how to ride a motorbike?"

"Who says?" he replied. "Who says I don't know how to ride? I can ride, Allie-boy, I can ride, ride, ride!" With that he clasped the phantom handlebars once again and *vroomed* off.

I didn't see much of him over the next few weeks. One day he drove into camp on a Norton motorcycle with his canvas dispatch bag slung over his shoulder. Most of our platoon soon surrounded him and he revved the motor and made everyone jealous. Then he did a quick circle around the camp and roared away towards the sea.

* * *

June 24, 1941

Dear Mum:

Just a quick note to ask you for a small favour. Mackie is in the hospital. He had an accident on his motorcycle, but it's not serious. He's broken his wrist and maybe a rib or two, so it may be a while before he writes to his family.

Would you mind popping across and telling Mrs. Mac that he's okay and she shouldn't worry? I've just seen him and he was telling jokes about it and says he'll be out in a couple of days.

The weather has turned warm here, a nice change after all the cold rain. With Hitler attacking Russia it looks like the Jerries won't be invading England anytime soon. I wonder what they'll do with us Canadians now?

Thanks for the package with the socks and the book and the homemade fudge. (My greedy mates thank you, too!)

Love,

Alistair

✳ ✳ ✳

"Hey, Mack," I said when I greeted him in his hospital bed, "even Lord Haw Haw knows about you!" He gave me a grin that turned into a wince, since half his face was bandaged and his arm was hanging from a pulley.

Lord Haw Haw was the nickname for an Englishman with a snooty accent who made propaganda radio broadcasts for the Germans. Some of the guys would listen in to hear what new rumours Haw Haw was spreading. The night before, he had said that it would be easy to eradicate the Canadian army. "Simply issue every Canadian soldier with a motorcycle and turn him loose," he quipped.

"It's those damn Harleys," said Mackie when I related this. "I liked the Nortons better."

The Americans had supplied the Canadian army with new Harley-Davidson motorcycles. They were powerful but had a low undercarriage, which meant they could bottom out on rough ground. Mackie had been roaring along the coastal road when he met a convoy of trucks coming around a curve. He swerved off the road and the Harley went haywire and sent him flying. Mackie said they'd found him near the top of the cliffs. His injuries were a little more serious than I'd described in my letter. His leg was in a big cast and it looked like it would be a while before he'd be walking again.

Mackie had planned to go up to Scotland with me on our next week's leave, but I had to catch the train for Glasgow without him. In the end it was just as well I was on my own. My memories of that trip are of sitting in damp parlours in front of smouldering coal fires (which always had china dogs on the mantel) sipping endless cups of tea with my relatives.

Mackie would have made a hasty retreat to the nearest pub in seconds flat if he'd been with me.

In the end, I decided to make my own escape and took the train to Edinburgh, where I walked up to the castle and around the narrow streets of the ancient city and felt proud to be a Scot.

In November Mackie rejoined our battalion, still limping a little. There was no talk of him returning to being a dispatch rider. Only a few days later we were loaded into trucks and transferred to a large estate in East Sussex called Oldlands Hall. We were billeted in one wing of the huge old mansion. Its owner, Sir Bernard Eckstein, lived with his servants in the main part of the house. Sir Bernard was a very wealthy man who had donated a Spitfire to the Royal Air Force. He was also a noted art collector, and the formal gardens of Oldlands Hall had classical statues surrounded by neatly trimmed hedges. I loved being in such a beautiful place and Mackie regained some of his energy and high spirits while we were there.

Lieutenant Whitman liked to speak with Sir Bernard and we sometimes saw them walking together in the gardens. Twitman always wore his suck-up smile and had his swagger stick tucked under his arm. One day after parade he pasted the smile on again and said to us, "I wish to have a word with you all about the village."

The village near Oldlands Hall was called Uckfield. It didn't take us long to guess what

Twitman's request was going to be. "Sir Bernard has asked me," Twitman continued, "to remind you that the name of the village is Uckfield. Just Uckfield. If you *must* add a certain consonant before the name of the village, we would ask that you *not* do so in front of the villagers."

We all laughed loudly, since Twitman's smile indicated that this was one of his having-a-laugh-with-the-chaps moments. I later got a big laugh myself at the local pub by sending up Twitman. "Chaps, if you simply *must* . . . "

Another big night at the pub came when we heard that Germany and the United States were at war. On December 7, 1941, the Japanese had attacked the American naval base at Pearl Harbor in Hawaii. When the Americans declared war on Japan, Germany — as an ally of Japan — declared war on the United States.

"The Yanks are in!" we cheered as we raised glasses of warm English beer.

"Now we'll give them a show!" crowed Pullio.

Everyone was saying that with the Yanks in the war, the Canadians would be sure to see some action soon. There was certain to be a big push coming. Unlike Mackie and the others, who wanted to see some "action," the prospect of real fighting filled me with dread.

CHAPTER 6

IN TRAINING

May 19, 1942

"Something's up!" announced Turnbull, one of our platoon-mates. "Basher's here. Looks like we're being shipped out."

We had hardly seen our commanding officer, Lt-Colonel Hedley Basher, since we had been sent to the south coast over a year ago. I remembered him standing stiffly erect on the parade ground in Aldershot with his huge St. Bernard, Royal, beside him.

Turnbull's news couldn't always be trusted, of course. A few weeks ago he'd heard "for sure, for certain" that the Canadians were being sent to fight in North Africa. Which never happened. So we had learned to separate the truth from Turnbull's bull. But it turned out that he was right this time. That morning before inspection, Lieutenant Whitman had told us to pack up our gear and report to the parade ground at 1100 hours for an address by our commanding officer. (Turnbull immediately put on his

63

I-told-you-so expression.) During the inspection, Mackie was missing.

"I see that Private McAllister is not gracing us with his presence this morning," said Whitman dryly. "Have him report to me as soon as he returns."

This wasn't the first time that Mackie had been absent without leave. He now had a girlfriend named Mavis that he saw whenever he could. It had been customary for Mackie to have several English girlfriends on the go — until he met Mavis at a dance just after we were transferred from Oldlands Hall in January to an army camp on Salisbury Plain, near the ancient monument of Stonehenge.

After a month on Salisbury Plain we were transferred south to Witley Camp, near a town called Horsham. On weekend leave, Mackie would take the train from Horsham up to Salisbury to see Mavis and sometimes he didn't make it back to camp till Monday morning. He'd been docked so much pay for being AWOL that he practically owed the army money. I began to worry that he might not show up before we were shipped out that morning.

As we packed up our gear, Turnbull said, "This could be it, boys! The Russkies want a Second Front to take the heat off of them. Time for us to have a go at Hitler!"

Overhearing this, Sergeant Hartley retorted, "Cut the baloney, Turnbull. We're not gonna be kicking Hitler's backside out of Paris anytime soon. We're just getting some special training so we can put on a show for the king and queen."

We all groaned and Pullio wisecracked, "Gee, I hope the two princesses get to come, too!"

I knew that there were many people who agreed with Turnbull. On a weekend leave in London I'd seen demonstrators in Trafalgar Square carrying banners that said *Second Front Now* and *Aid Our Russian Allies.* They thought that Britain should attack Nazi-occupied France to help the Russians, who were battling the German invaders. But Winston Churchill wasn't crazy enough to invade Hitler's Fortress Europe just yet, I thought. At least I hoped he wasn't.

By 1100 hours we were all lined up on the parade ground but there was still no sign of Mackie. Lt-Colonel Basher appeared with the other officers (and with a soldier holding Royal on a leash) and told us that the Royal Regiment was shipping out to join the entire 2nd Canadian Division for special combat training. He said that he was sure we would do the regiment proud and we all cheered and threw our caps in the air. Soon we were taking down tents and hauling our bags towards the khaki army trucks that had pulled into the camp. I was really getting worried about Mackie.

When most of our platoon was seated in a truck, I suddenly spied him sauntering among the tents. "Hey, Mack, Mack, over here!" I yelled. "See the sergeant. We're pulling out!" Then I saw Hartley leading Mackie off to the officers' quarters and my heart sank.

About twenty minutes passed while we all sat and waited. Then a kit bag was tossed into the truck, followed by Mackie, who swung himself down beside me. We all cheered and Mackie, looking perfectly relaxed, said, "Wouldn't wanna miss the show!"

As we rumbled down the country roads I asked him what had happened in the officers' quarters.

"Aw, nothin' much," he replied. "Twitman said he'd deal with me later and to get myself and my kit into a truck. So here I am!" He flashed his big grin and put me in a headlock, rubbing his fist in my hair.

"So how's Mavis?" I asked.

His face darkened. "Aww, well, not so good. She wants me to marry her, but she says she'd never leave England. I like her a lot, but not enough to become English," he said with a shrug.

After an hour or so we began to catch glimpses

of the sea, and soon saw signs for the city of Portsmouth. As our truck pulled into Portsmouth harbour there were hundreds of men in khakis with 2nd Division patches milling about between jeeps, Bren-gun carriers and scout cars.

"Holy cow," said Mackie, "this is some big shin-dig we're in for."

As we climbed down from the truck and hoisted our kit bags, Sergeant Hartley held up his hand and we followed him towards another group of Royals. We were then lined up and marched towards a large ferry. As we walked up the gang-way, I asked a sailor where we were headed.

"To the Isle of Wight, chum," he replied. "You're all off on a little 'oliday!"

I'd heard about the Isle of Wight, just off England's south coast. I knew that it was a popu-lar place for summer holidays, but was pretty sure that our combat training would be anything but a vacation. And yet we all felt in a holiday mood. After we got off the ferry in a town called Fishbourne, we climbed into trucks that took us through tiny, quaint villages with thatched cot-tages and square stone church towers. Someone started singing the Basher's Dashers song and we all joined in. Then the sun broke through between the clouds and sent shafts of light onto hillsides dotted with spring wildflowers and grazing sheep.

I could see why they called the Isle of Wight "England in miniature." Only 23 miles wide and 12 miles deep, the island is shaped like a teapot. We were heading towards Freshwater, a west coast village at the tip of the teapot's spout. There we were billeted in tiny holiday cottages that had sweeping views of a curving beach and white chalk cliffs. Our holiday mood was boosted even higher when we learned that the Royals were the first regiment to arrive on the island. Old Basher had acted so smartly when he received his orders that we had even landed a few hours ahead of General Hamilton Roberts, the 2nd Division's commanding officer.

The next day the other regiments began arriving. The Essex Scottish were bunking down in a holiday camp just up the road and the Royal Hamilton Light Infantry (nicknamed "the Rileys") were stationed in a village a few miles inland called Shorwell. Turnbull announced that the Calgary Tanks regiment was unloading Churchill tanks on Queen Victoria's former private bathing beach.

That afternoon we had time off so I took a long walk along the white cliffs above the sea. I discovered a tall granite cross that was a memorial to Alfred Lord Tennyson, the famous Victorian poet who had once lived nearby. The area was called Tennyson Down after him. I remembered old Miss McRae, my high school English teacher, reading his poem, "The Charge of the Light Brigade," to us in her quavering voice:

Theirs not to reason why,
Theirs but to do and die:
Into the valley of Death
Rode the six hundred.

That fatal cavalry charge had happened over eighty-five years ago — yet "theirs not to reason why" still seemed the British army's way of doing things, I thought to myself. I hoped that the "theirs but to do and die" part of the poem didn't still apply.

That evening we were told that the Isle of Wight had been sealed off to all visitors and that our mail would be strictly censored. Then we were shown a film called *The Next of Kin* that told of a commando raid that had failed because of careless talk. There was lots of whistling at the seductive blond actress who coaxed military secrets out of young soldiers and passed them to the enemy. But we were all quiet at the end when the troops were cut down by enemy gunfire.

The next day our training began in earnest at 0600 hours. And it was fiercer, tougher training than anything we'd experienced so far. For twelve hours each day we crawled through ditches and obstacle courses, made yelling bayonet charges at sandbag dummies and learned how to scale the white chalk cliffs using ropes and aluminum tube ladders. There was also a daily speed march that was a killer — 11 miles doing double time in full battle dress in hot weather. And every day they set faster targets for us. Sometimes old Basher would drive by and give orders from his car.

By the second week they were firing live bullets over our heads as we crawled under rolls of barbed wire — a quick lesson in how to keep our heads down. We practised with automatic weapons like Bren guns and Tommy guns and learned how to fire from the hip while running. We were also given a new submachine gun that everybody hated, called the Sten gun. We called it "the plumber's nightmare" because it looked like an odd assortment of pipes. Sten guns often jammed and would go off if they were dropped. One day a lieutenant was leading his men over a fence carrying his Sten when it went off and the bullet went right up his arm.

We also used live ammunition and threw grenades like baseballs while training in house-to-house fighting. For this we used a ruined village that had been bombed out during a raid by German planes. By early June, most of our time was spent doing practice runs of beach assaults. About thirty of us would be loaded into each of the blunt-ended landing craft that would then roar towards the beaches until grounded. The ramps would be kicked down and we would charge into the water carrying our weapons above our shoulders. Sometimes the water would be neck-high or even over our heads. Once I saw Mackie, who couldn't swim, floundering in deep water, but within minutes he was on the beach holding his rifle triumphantly over his head.

With all the hard training, Mackie didn't have much time to brood over Mavis. A group of us would often go into the pub in Freshwater in the evenings and Mackie was already flirting with several local girls. By now his limp was completely gone and his dancing was as wild as ever. We also met men from the Essex Scottish and other Canadian regiments and there was a real sense of comradeship from the hard training we were going through together. We didn't know exactly what we were preparing for, though nobody believed that it was just to put on a show for the king and queen. After so many months without action, we felt proud to be fighting men once again.

On the morning of June 11, Turnbull let everybody know that he'd heard "something big was up." Sure enough, that afternoon the khaki army trucks started pulling in near our little beach cottages and we were taken to Cowes. There we were told that the whole 2nd Division was taking part in a practice assault landing on the English coast. Its code name was Exercise Yukon. Steamers with landing craft on board were waiting in the harbour, and Churchill tanks were being loaded into one of them.

Once on board we were given our orders. At first light, there was to be a mock attack on either side of the town of Bridport in Dorset on England's southwest coast. We were then to advance inland and capture key targets.

By 0300 hours we were a few miles off the Dorset coast, in rough seas. A baby-faced soldier we all called Smiler became seasick and vomited on Murphy's leg. Murphy swore at him but then the smell made him vomit too.

Before dawn, the sea had calmed a little, and the landing craft were lowered for us to go ashore. As we sped towards the coast we could just make out the pebbled beach ahead and hear the waves breaking on it. When the ramp was thrown down we charged into the water and onto the beach, just as we had practised so many times. But there was no firing from any of the English forces who were supposed to be "defending" the coast from attack. We soon overran the gun emplacements above the shore, taking the English soldiers completely by surprise. As they held up their hands, Whitman approached the sergeant in charge, who seemed completely flummoxed by the whole thing.

Another of our lieutenants, Ryerson, was poring over his map. "We've landed in the wrong place!" he called out to Whitman. "There should be a church steeple over there," he said, pointing his finger. "We're about two miles away from our target!"

Whitman vented his anger on the poor English sergeant who was standing there with his hands up and who knew nothing about Exercise Yukon.

"We could have been Germans!" Whitman spat. "What if this had been *real?*"

The sergeant asked if Whitman was going to report him. "No, I won't," Whitman replied in his best English accent, "but wake up, man, this is *your* country!"

"Yeah, right, Twitman," Mackie whispered to me, "they coulda been on the alert and *shot* us!"

Whitman wheeled around red-faced and barked out, "Let's go, men, on the double. We have *time* to make up!" We trotted off westward and, about twenty minutes later, reached the beach where we should have landed originally. But we weren't the only ones who were late. The South Saskatchewan Regiment and the Queen's Own Cameron Highlanders from Winnipeg had also been put ashore in the wrong place. And the big landing craft with the Calgary Tanks on board hadn't even come ashore yet. Exercise Yukon seemed to be a bit of a shambles. Turnbull later reported that there had been some top-brass generals watching from the cliffs and that Ham Roberts had been very embarrassed.

"Aww, gee, I feel so-o bad for him," jeered Pullio and we all chuckled.

"It was the British navy guys who screwed up, though," Mackie pointed out. "They put us ashore in the wrong place."

We returned to our camp on the Isle of Wight and the speed marches and beach assault practices resumed. Ten days later we were told there was going to be another big practice manoeuvre, to be called Yukon II. So on June 22 we were once again trucked to Cowes, put on the same ships as before and sent to the same bay in Dorset. This time the seas were calm so there was no vomiting and the British navy crew put us ashore in the right place. We landed just before dawn on the beach that had been our target before, and managed to overrun the gun positions and move inland and take our targets in the town of Bridport. Although our part of the exercise went quite smoothly, we heard that the landing craft carrying the Essex Scottish had gotten lost and that some of the troops had once again landed late.

"Way to go, Navy," Smiler scoffed.

"Well, let's hope the brass are happy," said Murphy, referring to the generals who had once again been watching from the clifftops. "We did our part perfectly!"

As we sailed back to Cowes under a perfect blue sky, dozing shirtless on the decks in the hot sun, we certainly felt happy. And we felt proud of what we were able to do. I thought back to my last leave home after Camp Borden, when I'd overheard a neighbour say to my mother, "Well, the Army certainly seems to be making a man of your Alistair!" This had made me cringe at the time, but now I felt as if this just might be true.

CHAPTER 7

OPERATION RUTTER

July 2, 1942

"Another exercise? They gotta be kidding!" muttered Pullio. "How many times can we *do* this?"

"Ours is not to reason why," I replied as I rolled up my sleeping bag on the floor of our tiny holiday hut. We had been told to pack up all our gear as we were leaving Freshwater. I felt sorry to be saying goodbye to such a beautiful place in the height of summer.

Soon the familiar army trucks rumbled into camp and we tossed in our bags and climbed aboard. This time we went only a few miles up the road to Yarmouth, a small port on the Solent, the sea channel that separates the Isle of Wight from England. Yarmouth had a famous long pier, built of huge timbers in Victorian times, and the trucks drove right onto it.

Dozens of military ships were anchored in the Solent as all five thousand infantry of the 2nd Division were to take part in Exercise Klondike, as this newest practice was to be called. Two large ferries were waiting for us. The Royals in the trucks ahead of us were boarding one called the *Princess Josephine Charlotte*. We were directed to the second one, the *Princess Astrid*. Once we were all on board, the *Astrid* pulled away from the pier and lowered her anchor offshore in the Solent near the *Princess Josephine Charlotte*. At 1800 hours we all gathered belowdecks where Lt-Colonel Basher and the other officers were standing before a large map.

When all was quiet, Basher stepped forward. "Men," he said, "this is not an exercise. There will be no Exercise Klondike. The Royal Regiment of Canada is about to take part in Operation Rutter. Together with the other regiments of the Canadian 2nd Division, we will strike a blow at Adolf Hitler's Fortress Europe."

The room went wild. We whooped, we hugged each other and threw our hats in the air. After all our practices, route marches, endless drills with barked-out commands, this was the real thing, at last! Basher waited patiently with a half-smile on his stern face. Then he pointed his swagger stick at the map behind him. "Operation Rutter is a reconnaissance in force, *not* an invasion. The target is the port of Dieppe on the coast of France, sixty-six miles across the English Channel. We will land before dawn, capture key targets and enemy prisoners, obtain valuable information and withdraw within six hours. There will be full air and naval support."

We cheered again — this was sounding easy! A couple of guys muttered "a piece of cake!" Basher pointed his swagger stick at Dieppe on the map and said, "There will be eight assaults along a ten-mile front. The Royal Regiment, assisted by the men of the Black Watch, will land here, on a beach code-named Blue," he said, tapping the map with his stick. "Blue Beach is one mile to the east of the town of Dieppe. We will take the enemy by surprise, eliminate four anti-aircraft gun positions and one artillery battery that is code-named Rommel. We will thus secure and hold the eastern headland above Dieppe before the landings on the main town beachfronts. More detailed orders will be given to you by your officers tomorrow."

The mood remained jubilant as men slapped each other on the back. But it didn't sound like "a piece of cake" to me. As I walked back to where I'd laid out my sleeping bag on the deck, I ran through what Basher had said. It sounded to me as if everything had to go like clockwork.

"What if we can't knock out those enemy guns?" I said to Mackie. "And what if we *don't* take them by surprise?"

"Aww, Allie," he replied. "You think too much. We'll have lots of cover from the RAF boys. And the Navy'll be blasting away with their big guns. We'll find out more tomorrow, just wait."

The next day was sunny and hot. We had to stay belowdecks, out of sight of enemy aircraft. In the humid, stifling air deep inside the ship, it was hard to concentrate on the briefings from the officers. And what I was hearing didn't make me feel any easier about our mission. In addition to destroying the four gun emplacements and the Rommel battery above Blue Beach, we also had to take out a number of machine-gun positions *and* a German barracks. All in thirty minutes! And if we failed, the Essex Scottish and the Rileys would be trapped in a crossfire when they came ashore on Dieppe's main beachfronts. But I said nothing — I was only a lowly private. And I didn't want any of the others thinking I was a coward.

That evening our whole ship was given a big boost by a visit from Lord Louis Mountbatten, the Chief of Combined Operations. Mountbatten was responsible for planning all enemy raids, and Operation Rutter was his baby. He entered the room with Ham Roberts. But all eyes were on Admiral Mountbatten. Tall, slim and dark-haired, he looked like he'd stepped out of an

English war movie. His impeccable dress white summer uniform had two rows of brass buttons on the front and gold braid on the shoulders. He had a chestful of medals. We'd all heard about Mountbatten's exploits as commander of the HMS *Kelly*, a destroyer that had been sunk during the Battle of Crete the year before. And I knew that he was part of the royal family, one of the king's many cousins.

As soon as Mountbatten opened his mouth there was no mistaking that he was an aristocrat. He had one of those elegant English accents that make Canadians feel like wood choppers from the colonies. Yet he was obviously used to putting ordinary soldiers and sailors at ease. He began by telling a joke which wasn't all that funny, but right before the punchline Whitman let out a loud braying laugh that convulsed the whole room.

After the laughter died down, Mountbatten continued his address. "I was on the destroyers in the early part of the war," he said, "and I know what it felt like when some admiral who'd been sucking his teeth onshore for months came aboard to tell us how to fight. I'm not going to tell you how to fight, because you *know* how."

We cheered at this and Mountbatten went on to say how fond he was of Canada and Canadians and how he knew we were the kind of chaps who would bring it all off. We stood and cheered again and whistled and everyone (including me) felt very fired up about Operation Rutter. Ham Roberts then stood up (looking squat and stolid after Mountbatten) and told us that Operation Rutter would launch at 0430 hours the next morning. Afterwards I noticed Whitman, wearing his biggest suck-up smile ever, elbowing his way through the other officers so he could shake Mountbatten's hand.

* * *

During the night I kept waking up, thinking it was time for us to leave for France. When Sergeant Hartley finally roused us I saw that the sun was already shining.

"It's been postponed for a day," Mackie told me. "The weather's not right."

"Gee, it looks okay to me," I said sleepily, looking out at the blue sky and calm waters of the Solent.

"The winds are wrong for the paratroopers," announced the all-knowing Turnbull. I then remembered from the briefings that British paratroopers were to be dropped first to take out the big gun batteries at either end of the assault front before we landed. I guessed that the winds could easily blow them off target.

Another hot, humid day followed, with more map briefings belowdecks and with the same orders being gone over once again. Then we checked and re-checked our equipment. I was glad to be just a rifleman. Mackie was carrying a Bren gun, which had to be taken apart and cleaned and lubricated quite regularly. I also felt sorry for the guys with Sten guns, who had to carefully file down and calibrate each part of their weapons to coax them into working properly. And all of us carefully filed and sharpened our knives and bayonets and inserted the detonators into our grenades to get them ready for action.

That evening when they announced another twenty-four-hour postponement there were more loud groans. "You never had better weather in your bathtub!" I overheard one officer exclaim grumpily. The following morning, the *Princess Astrid* lifted anchor and took us back to the pier for a route march. As we tramped around the country roads outside Yarmouth, I said to Mackie, "I thought we were *done* with this!"

"Not us, Allie, not us, we're just PBI," he responded. I had to laugh — Poor Bloody Infantry was exactly what we were.

Despite all the griping it was good to be off the stifling ship and marching past flowering hedgerows in the July sunshine. In the afternoon we went back on the *Astrid,* and that evening heard that weather conditions were still not right. How much longer can this drag on? we all wondered. That night was another hot one and I slept on deck once again.

Early the next morning I heard the buzzing sound of an aircraft in the distance. Half-dreaming, I thought I was back at Camp Borden and it was one of the pilots there on a training run. Suddenly there was a screaming roar overhead and the whole ship shuddered. "It's the Jerries!" someone yelled, "We've been hit!" just as a bomb crashed through the top deck and onto ours. But it didn't explode. It ricocheted across the deck towards where Murphy was lying and ran right down the side of his leg. Murphy screamed and writhed and I could smell something burning. The bomb then skidded off the side of the deck and fell into the water, where it exploded.

I ran over to Murphy, but Mackie was already cradling his head. "It's okay, Murph. It's okay, you saved us Murph, the bomb's gone," he repeated as Murphy whimpered with pain. "Allie, get help!" Mackie shouted, but two men with a stretcher were already racing down the deck. As I looked over the rail I saw a second German plane swooping upwards, away from the *Princess Josephine Charlotte*. I could make out the Nazi swastika on its tail. "They've hit the *Charlotte*, too!" I yelled.

A medic began cutting Murphy's pants off. Another one jabbed a needle into his arm and he soon became quiet.

"His leg's burned," said Mackie, turning to me. "But he's gonna be okay."

We felt the rumble of the *Astrid*'s engines and within minutes we were beside the pier. The *Princess Josephine Charlotte* was pulling in behind us, her hull low in the water. Trucks and ambulances were racing into the harbour and I could see men running along the pier. Murphy was carried off in a stretcher. Several wounded men were helped down the gangway from the *Charlotte*. The bomb had crashed right down into its engine room and out through the bottom of the ship and exploded in the water underneath it, flooding the engine room.

As we waited on the pier for further instructions, we heard that there were only four Royals injured from the bombing raid, none of them seriously, and some crewmen on the *Charlotte* as well. We talked about how much worse it could have been if the bombs had hit any of our rounds of ammunition. But now neither ship was in any shape to take us into battle.

Early in the afternoon, we loaded our bags and equipment into trucks. We were then put into formation and the whole regiment began marching in the direction of Cowes. After an hour or so, a motorcycle approached and when it met up with Lt-Colonel Basher's jeep at the head of the column, the dispatch rider dismounted and gave him an envelope. Basher read it and within seconds the word "cancelled" rippled down the long column of men. We gathered round to hear what we thought we already knew.

"The operation against Dieppe has been cancelled," Basher announced, standing up in his jeep. "We are to return to camp in England."

"No, no, no!" erupted from the mouths of five hundred and fifty men almost in unison.

Mackie threw down his pack in disgust. Smiler went and lay face down in a nearby field. A red-faced Pullio kept jabbing his bayonet fiercely into a hedgerow until Hartley told him to stop. A few men sat by the roadside with their heads in their hands. Some, I think, were crying.

But all I could feel was an enormous, overwhelming sense of relief.

CHAPTER 8
OPERATION JUBILEE
August 13, 1942

As the train crossed the border into Scotland, Mackie grabbed me by the shoulders and woke me. "Scots wha hae, laddie!" he said in an imitation Scottish accent, "Scots wha hae!"

"What's up? Oh right, we're in Scotland. Great," I mumbled before putting my head back against the window and dozing again.

We were on our first leave since the regiment had returned to England after the cancellation of Operation Rutter. Mackie had wanted to visit Scotland ever since we'd arrived there off the ship almost two years ago. But with his motorcycle accident and then being confined to barracks because of all his AWOL infractions, he hadn't made it. I wasn't even sure he would be given leave this time. Two days before, however, he had scored the winning home run for the Royals in a baseball game against the Essex Scottish at Horsham. For this he had received a big clap on the back from Lt-Colonel Douglas

Catto, who had just replaced Basher as our commanding officer. Basher had left camp after being replaced by his younger second-in-command. Turnbull said that lots of older officers were being replaced in the Canadian army by younger men. We all liked Catto, but somehow "Catto's Dashers" didn't have quite the same ring to it.

For our leave we had agreed to skip seeing relatives and just have fun and do some sightseeing in Glasgow and Edinburgh. This was fine with me, since I couldn't bear the thought of more cups of tea with old aunties. Mackie also wanted to catch a train to Inverness to see some Highland scenery. Hearing about our plans, Smiler and Pullio had decided to come along as well. Murphy was still recovering from his burns in hospital, but we heard that he was doing well.

In Glasgow we visited the Clydeside shipyards, since Mackie wanted to see where big ships like the *Queen Mary* and *Queen Elizabeth* had been built. He said his grandfather had worked there. Near the river Clyde we could see some tangled wreckage from enemy bombing raids. But we could hear hammering as construction of new ships for the Navy continued. I also took Mackie and the others to see the red sandstone tenement house that we had lived in before we emigrated to Canada.

In Edinburgh, Mackie, Pullio and Smiler were very impressed with all the grand buildings and kept saying how they liked it much better than Glasgow. (Being Glasgow-born, this annoyed me slightly, but I couldn't disagree with them as Glasgow had looked a little shabby.) For a good view of Auld Reekie, as Edinburgh was nick-named, we climbed to the top of Arthur's Seat, a rocky escarpment near Holyrood Palace. On the way back to our hotel we passed a large hostel where servicemen could stay on leave. Smiler suggested we go in for a free cup of tea.

"You lads are with the Royal Regiment of Canada?" asked the woman at the front desk. "I think I've got a message for you." We gave each other puzzled looks until then she came back with a telegram she had posted on the bulletin board. It stated that all men of the Canadian 2nd Division were ordered to return to camp immediately.

We all groaned and glared accusingly at Smiler. Our plans for the evening had been to go out and meet some Edinburgh lassies. Instead we found ourselves waiting on the train platform for the next train south. We wondered what was up. Could it just be another manoeuvre? There wasn't likely to be another operation like Rutter anytime soon. The aborted raid on Dieppe had been blabbed about all over the British Isles by now, so the enemy would certainly be aware of it.

We didn't arrive in camp until noon the next day, the 17th of August. Lieutenant Whitman told us that we were leaving tomorrow on another big manoeuvre. So once again we began preparing our weapons and ammunition. The much-hated Sten guns had been in storage since Rutter and were covered in black grease, so all the parts had to be cleaned and reassembled. The trucks came for us after lunch the next day and we loaded all our gear on board. Once we were inside, something different happened. The khaki tarpaulins were lowered and tied down over the backs of each truck so no one could see us. It made for a rather hot and gloomy ride. But within an hour I could smell the sea. Were we going back to the Isle of Wight, I wondered.

When our truck stopped and the tarp was opened I saw that we were in Portsmouth harbour. Then I spotted the same cross-channel ferries in the harbour. It looked like they had assault landing craft on board. We were marched towards one of them, the *Princess Astrid* — the same ship we had been on when the bomb hit. Clearly they had managed to repair the damage to her decks. As we boarded, an English sailor said, "You know where, we're headed? It's Dieppe! Dieppe!"

Thinking he was joking, I smiled and replied, "Nope, that was *last* time!"

On board, however, everyone was talking about us going back to Dieppe.

I said to Mackie, "Is this for real? Won't the Germans know we're coming?"

"Maybe they figure Dieppe is the *last* place we'd attack," he replied.

"Yeah, *right*," I said skeptically.

Looking over the railing at all the activity in the harbour, I caught sight of the masts and rigging of HMS *Victory*, the old wooden flagship of Admiral Nelson. The *Victory* had been kept in Portsmouth harbour as a memorial to Nelson, who had died on board it during the Battle of Trafalgar over a hundred and thirty years ago. I thought back to the statue of Nelson atop the monument in Trafalgar Square, hoping for Nelson's luck and victory once again.

After a meal of some stew and bread, we were given a briefing about Operation Jubilee — the new name for the remounted Dieppe raid. This time there was no whooping and cheering from us. Everyone just seemed grimly determined to get on with the job and get it over with. The plans seemed the same as last time except that British commandos, instead of paratroopers, were going to take out the big guns to the east and west of Dieppe. At least we wouldn't have any more delays waiting for the winds to be right. With maps and aerial photographs, Lt-Colonel Catto went over the plans for our landing on Blue Beach below the village of Puys. We were told we wouldn't need our gas masks and that carrying water bottles would be optional, as we would only be in France for a few hours.

Everyone seemed calm, almost as if we were on another manoeuvre. We were told that pens and paper were available so we could write a letter home, and that we should note at the top: *To be mailed only if I fail to return.* I decided to write to my mother and I realized, while doing so, that it could be my last letter. Only then did the reality of what we were about to do begin to sink in.

TO BE MAILED ONLY IF I FAIL TO RETURN

Mrs. Angus Morrison
64 Hiawatha Road
Toronto, Ontario
August 18, 1942

Dear Mum,

I am writing this on board the troop carrier Princess Astrid. *We are finally going to see some* action and are heading for Dieppe, a German-held port on the French coast. There are hundreds of ships taking part in this operation. Everyone is calm and we have trained hard for this for weeks.

You will likely have read about the raid in the newspapers by the time you get this letter. If I've been taken prisoner, I don't want you to worry. We've been carefully trained on what to do as prisoners of war. It will be boring, but the war won't last forever.

If you're reading this letter because I haven't made it, then there are a few things I'd like you to know. I want to say I'm sorry that I upset you by joining up without telling you first. I've thought many times about your saying to me, "You're not the army type." Well, you know me better than anyone, and you're right, I'm not the army type. I don't like all the shouting and the endless drills and always being told what to do.

But I want you and Elspeth and Doreen to know that I don't regret any of it. The last two years in England have been just a great experience for me. I've seen places that I might only have read about — the Tower of London, Edinburgh Castle, Stonehenge and the Isle of Wight. I feel that I've been part of an important time in the history of the world. I've met unforgettable people here in England

and made many good friends. There's nothing like army training to make you trust and depend on your buddies.

I know you blame Mackie for getting me into this, but he has been the best of friends to me, helping me with everything. Tell his mum that he is one of the most admired and popular soldiers in our battalion.

Finally, I want to thank you for being such a good, loving mother to me and the girls. I know in our family we don't often say these things. It's not the Scottish way. But I couldn't have asked for a better mother. I think of you every day and will love you always.

God Bless You.

All my love to Elspeth and Doreen.

Your loving son,

Alistair Morrison B67757
'B' Company
Royal Regiment of Canada

CHAPTER 9

BLUE MURDER

August 18, 1942, 2220 hours

I went out on the stern deck to prime my two grenades. Each of us was taking turns doing this. It always made me nervous, as it was a ticklish job. I took a deep breath and inserted a detonator into the first grenade. I paused and then did the same with the second one. Neither exploded. I put them into grenade pouches and attached them both to my webbing.

A sliver of moon broke through the clouds and I could just make out the shapes of the other ships advancing silently across the sea. It was rare for the Channel to be as calm as this — as flat as a mill-pond, I'd heard people say. Maybe it was a good omen. I looked out in the darkness and wondered just how many ships were crossing with us. There had to be at least two hundred, carrying about six thousand men into battle. Some of those men aren't coming back, I thought — that's what happens in war. For them, this warm summer night will be their last night on earth. Could I be one of them? Will my life be over tomorrow? I wondered if everyone was thinking this or whether some men just blocked it out. These thoughts made my guts start to churn, so I decided to rejoin the others inside.

My Lee-Enfield and bayonet and two bandoliers of bullets lay against the bulkhead where I'd left them. The other men in the platoon were sitting quietly; there was none of the usual joking and chatter. Tea and a washtub of sandwiches had been put out for us, but nobody seemed hungry. A few were still writing letters that would return with the *Astrid*.

I sat down next to Mackie. He passed me two metal hand mirrors.

"Put one in each pocket," he said quietly, pointing to the breast pockets on my battle jacket. "A little extra protection."

"What about you?" I asked. He just smiled and looked away. I took one and put it in the pocket over his heart.

Just before midnight, we heard a change in the throbbing noise of the ship's engines.

"We must be entering the minefield," said Turnbull.

We knew that minesweepers were out in front to

lead us through the mines the Germans had laid off the French coast. This minefield was designed to provide a safe channel down the coast for their convoys going into French ports. We also knew that a large ship like the *Astrid* was more at risk of hitting a mine than some of the smaller ones. For the next hour we sat silently, listening for every noise. Finally we heard the ship's engines pick up speed, indicating that we'd made it through the minefield.

Around 0230 hours, Sergeant Hartley told us it was time to get ready. We began picking up our weapons and strapping on our webbing and ammo bandoliers. When I put on the inflatable lifebelt over it all, I felt like a bulky, shuffling robot. Out on the deck I saw that the moon had disappeared and we were in almost total darkness. Silently, we crept forward in single file, holding on to the bayonet scabbard of the man ahead. The landing craft had been swung out over the side and we were helped across the gap by British sailors. We took our seats in rows — one row down the centre and two on either side. I was in the stern on the port side and I could see a line of helmets ahead of me and feel the breathing of the men around me. With a whirring noise our landing craft was lowered down the side of the ship and into the water. Then I felt a rumble as its engines started up and we began to move away from the *Astrid*. The sky was dark, with a few stars overhead. I let the breeze cool my cheeks, as I was sweating underneath all my gear.

Our landing craft moved forward for about fifteen minutes, then abruptly changed direction. I later learned that we had lined up behind the wrong gunboat. When the British naval officer in charge of landing us discovered his mistake, the boats picked up speed to make up for lost time. I remembered how we had been put ashore in the wrong place during the Yukon I exercise, and hoped that this kind of confusion wouldn't happen again.

Suddenly, a white flare shot up into the sky.

It reminded me of the first rocket at the start of the Victoria Day fireworks show in Toronto. Then we heard the crackle of gunfire and some loud explosions. I turned to give a what's-up look to Mackie, but couldn't see him in the darkness. For the next ten minutes we listened to the sounds of a firefight at sea. It was hard to tell how close it was to us. Was this a part of Operation Jubilee? Only later would we learn that the gunboat leading the British commandos towards Yellow Beach had run into a German convoy. By the time the firing stopped, the boats carrying the commandos had been scattered and the gunboat severely damaged. Crouched in our own landing craft, we simply wondered whether our attack had been discovered.

Soon I saw the harbour lights of Dieppe on the horizon. As they came closer we changed direction once again and headed east towards Puys and Blue Beach. But the sky was beginning to lighten behind the looming cliffs on the coast. If we didn't attack before dawn, the Germans would see us coming! I could feel my heart thumping against the steel mirror in my pocket.

As we drew in towards the shore, a light flashed out a signal. Were we friend or foe? A moment passed and blinding lights swept out towards us. Then came the rattle of machine guns from onshore. Searchlights were sweeping the beach where the first boats were arriving. The gunfire died down briefly, then picked up again as the first men hit the beach. They won't stand a chance! I thought. Are we still going to land?

As we drew closer, bullets began hitting the side of our landing craft. It sounded like hail on a tin roof. The man beside me recoiled as the bullets pinged the steel hull only inches from him. There was smoke and men yelling and engines roaring as they tried to bring the landing craft closer to the beach. When the engines stopped, Lieutenant

Whitman stood up in the front of our boat with his pistol drawn. A bullet hit his helmet and knocked him back into his seat. The landing ramp was kicked down and Whitman stood up again, but as he turned his head towards us and raised his hand, a sniper's bullet sliced through his throat. A puzzled look crossed his face. Blood blossomed from his neck. Then he crumpled and fell into the water.

A second later machine-gun fire ricocheted right down the centre row of our boat. Men howled and fell over; blood began running in the channels on the floor.

Sergeant Hartley was a few rows ahead of me on the same side. He turned and yelled to us, "Stay and we're dead! Up and go! Let's go, go, GO!"

We grabbed our weapons and stumbled over the men lying in the boat. On the landing ramp were more bodies so I jumped off the side. The water was so cold! I sank to the bottom and gulped in salt water. Spitting and choking I kicked upwards, holding my rifle aloft. Dawn now fully lit the sky.

I spied a landing craft ahead that could provide some cover and waded forward. Suddenly I saw Smiler, his head leaning against the side of the boat. He gave me a wan version of his customary smile. I looked down and saw blood seeping into the water. Smiler was holding onto his stomach, trying to keep his intestines from coming out through a gaping wound. "Smiler!" I called out. "I'll get help! Wait here!"

Groggily he replied, "No, Allie, no . . . it's no good. You save yourself . . . You just go . . . You go."

As I hesitated beside Smiler there was a sudden screaming roar overhead. One of our Spitfires swooped down to strafe the gun positions onshore. This is my chance! I thought, splashing onto the pebbled beach past bodies rolling in the surf. Then I spied Sergeant Hartley lying below a hummock of beach stones, firing a Bren gun. I raced over and flopped down beside him. "Get to the seawall," he yelled just as a bullet tore through my battle jacket, grazing my side. As I crawled forward I heard another plane overhead and spotted heavy smoke dropping down from it. A smoke-screen! Thank God! I thought. Through the smoke I ran towards the seawall, stumbling over the bodies that lay in twisted positions in front of it. I noticed an officer crouched next to one of the stone buttresses that jutted out at right angles from the wall. I flopped down beside him.

"Aim for the white house!" he yelled over the noise, pointing to a two-storey house on the cliffs.

I threw off my life jacket and set my rifle on my shoulder. I could see the flash of machine-gun fire coming from the upper windows of the house. I fired a few rounds but the building seemed to be out of range. Then a mortar shell thudded down on the beach beside us, throwing a geyser of beach stones and dirt in our faces.

"Grab that Tommy gun!" shouted the officer, a lieutenant named Wedd. He motioned towards a weapon that lay next to a body on the beach. I waited out the next volley and then dashed towards the gun. Just as I grabbed it, bullets kicked up the stones around me and something raked across the back of my hand. I grabbed the gun and scurried back to the shelter of the buttress. On the way I leapt over a white, dead face with its mouth open. In a flash I realized it was Turnbull. Another of our men killed! In a blinding rage, I leaned out and fired the Tommy gun at the black slit of a pillbox gun nest that lay beyond the seawall. When I'd emptied the magazine, I stopped and licked the blood running down the back of my hand, and wiggled my fingers. Apart from a few deep cuts, the hand was fine.

"Give me a grenade!" Lieutenant Wedd yelled. I passed him both of my grenades and he attached one to his webbing and placed the other in his palm. He crawled around our buttress and started to inch along the seawall. The pillbox spat bullets at him whenever he moved. Each time, he flattened himself against the wall. I watched in amazement as he worked his way from one buttress to the next. Finally he made a dash towards the pillbox and threw a grenade into its dark slit. His body jerked upwards and then fell forward as bullets tore into him. He twitched on the ground and then lay still. A second later the pillbox blew out in a shower of flame and smoke. I was stunned, and humbled, by Wedd's courage.

A number of men who had been pinned down on the beach now made a rush for the seawall. Hartley was one of them, with Pullio running right behind him. Just as Hartley jumped down beside me, Pullio let out a howl and fell over. "I'm hit, I'm hit!" he screamed, clutching his leg. Hartley and I reached out and pulled him in towards us. One leg was shattered below the knee and blood was pouring down over his boot. Pullio's thrashing around drew enemy fire. Bullets thudded into the bodies lying nearby.

"Morrison! Get a stretcher, get him outta here!" yelled Hartley.

I looked around and saw a stretcher lying about 30 yards down the wall. Imitating what Wedd had done, I crawled around the buttress and then inched down the seawall, flattening myself against it as bullets pinged off the beach stones. Unlike Wedd, I was moving down the wall and away from the worst of the gunfire. As I crept around buttresses and edged farther along the wall, the firing towards me slowed. Finally I ran and dropped down next to the stretcher. The man who had been carrying one end of it was dead. I asked the other stretcher-bearer, McCluskey, if he could help me move someone and he nodded. I folded up the stretcher and slung it under one arm. McCluskey followed me as we inched our way back along the wall.

Ahead of us, I caught a glimpse of two of our men attempting to scale the wall. I knew they were aiming to lay an explosive charge in the rolls of barbed wire stretched on top of it. Their activity was drawing heavy machine-gun fire, which allowed us to move along the wall fairly unnoticed. Just as we reached Pullio I heard a cry from one of the soldiers climbing the wall. I glanced up to see him slide down to the beach, where he lay still. Hartley was trying to give the climbers some cover with his Tommy gun. Then I heard a small explosion and saw that a hole had been blown in the barbed wire. One man was already scrambling up to go through it. I motioned to McCluskey and we put Pullio on the stretcher and headed down the wall as quickly as we could.

When we reached the end of the seawall, we saw Lt-Colonel Catto with about twelve men. They had put a tube ladder up where the wall met the cliff. One man at the top was trying to hack through the barbed wire with cutters. Suddenly a mortar shell landed near us and we scurried against the cliff face for cover. Pullio whimpered as we ran with him, but otherwise lay still.

"There's a medic station down there," one of Catto's men yelled, "down with the Black Watch."

We moved on to where he pointed, staying close to the cliff face. Soon we started to see the men of the Black Watch who had landed at this end of the beach as reinforcements. We passed a signalman with his radio on his back and heard him repeating, "Attack on Blue Beach stalled, can you get us off? Over. . . . Attack on Blue Beach stalled . . . "

We were directed along the cliff to a medic station that had been set up in a small cave. There we found an officer doing his best to treat the wounded as quickly as he could. His white apron was drenched with blood. I showed him Pullio's leg and he immediately gave him a shot of morphine and began cutting away at his pant leg. I patted Pullio on the shoulder, gave him a thumbs-up and left.

McCluskey and I came out of the cave to more gunfire. A few mortar shells exploded nearby. The Black Watch tried to return fire but their weapons were out of range. McCluskey decided to stay with them but I thought I should try and rejoin Hartley. I also wanted to find Mackie. I was worried that I'd seen nothing of him that morning. As I moved along the cliff face some rocks tumbled down and I looked up and saw German soldiers running along the cliff-top. They began throwing down stick grenades. One of them landed near me. I scooped it up and threw it out onto the beach, where it exploded in a shower of stones. I was relieved I hadn't hit anyone with it.

As I scrambled along to the beginning of the sea-wall I noticed that the tube ladder was still there and spotted a small hole in the barbed wire. No soldiers were nearby so I hoped that they had gotten through. As I moved along to the first buttress, I noticed that it had suddenly gone quiet. The relentless firing had stopped. Then I heard some bellowing in German through a loud hailer.

"They're telling us to surrender," said a man crouched nearby.

"Tell them to go to Hell!" shouted another voice near the wall.

As if on cue we heard the loud, distinctive bark of the Royals' regimental sergeant-major. "Go . . . To . . . Hell!" he shouted back.

"You tell 'em, Murray!" called a couple of men.

The bellowed order in German was repeated a few minutes later. This time there was a long silence in response. Twisted bodies lay all along the beach. We could hear the moans of wounded men. The tide was coming in and some of the men were being drowned in the surf. There was no sign of any boats coming to rescue us.

The third time the command was given in heavily-accented English. "Zis is your last chance to surrender."

Silence followed. Then we saw a white under-shirt being raised on a bayonet. It was slowly waved back and forth three or four times. I heard a man near me sobbing.

It was over.

CHAPTER 10

SURRENDER

August 19, 1942, 0830 hours

Men in green uniforms swarmed onto the beach. The unseen enemy was suddenly everywhere.

"Ditch your knives," hissed one of the Royals near me.

I wasn't carrying a commando knife, but several soldiers pulled them out of their boots and began burying them in the beach pebbles. We knew that commandos could be shot on sight.

Ladders were lowered over the seawall and suddenly a young German soldier was standing in front of me.

"*Hände auf den Kopf!*" he spat out, gesturing upwards with his rifle.

I knew very little German, but understood enough to put my hands on my head. Other men near me slowly did the same.

"*Sofort, ihr werdet erschossen!*" he barked.

"Quickly, or you will be shot!" ordered another German soldier who spoke some English.

They rounded up about ten of us and we walked or limped towards the beach entrance to the village. The water from the incoming tide was red from the blood of the men bobbing in it. Suddenly I saw Smiler — he was moving in the waves as if he might be alive.

"My friend!" I cried, gesturing to the German soldier who spoke some English. "He is my friend!"

The soldier nodded so I dashed into the surf and pulled Smiler onto the beach. Another Royal grabbed his legs and we moved him up farther and laid him down. But Smiler was dead, his face utterly white. I placed his cold hands on his chest and closed his eyes. He looked so young, like a choirboy. We used to tease Smiler because he had to shave only once a week. I felt my shoulders heave. I didn't want the Germans to see me cry so I put a hand across my eyes, but the tears poured through my fingers. I fell to one knee. "Dear God," I whispered, "please look after Smiler. He's the best of boys."

"*Komm, komm!*" called one of the Germans, urging us forward. I stood up and placed my hands on my head and walked away from Smiler and all the bodies by the wall. At the entrance to the village the barbed-wire barriers had been pulled open enough for us to walk through. I saw a concrete gun nest that only minutes ago had been hurling fire at us. Before it lay the bodies of three men who had died trying to silence it. One of them was Sergeant Hartley. I pictured him charging at it, yelling and firing the Tommy gun from his hip. Poor, brave Hartley, I thought.

Suddenly there was a commotion behind us. Some of the Royals were gesturing, wanting to go back to the beach to pick up the wounded. But the Germans were refusing. I immediately thought of Mackie. What if he were lying on the beach bleeding to death? I ran back. The German soldiers were becoming agitated and gesturing with their weapons. We shouted and pointed to the beach, but the Germans yelled and jabbed us with their bayonets. Slowly we turned and walked up the main street with our hands on our heads.

Empty holiday homes with boarded-up windows stood on the steep hills on either side of the road. People used to spend their vacations here, I thought. I glanced up at the white stucco house near the cliffs, but could see no weapons pointing out its windows. Ahead lay another pillbox sunk into the roadway, its gun slit aimed towards the beach.

Out of the sky behind us a British Spitfire roared in from the sea. "A little late, chum!" someone shouted as we turned and looked up. But the plane suddenly swooped down towards the rooftops and began strafing us! We dived for cover and a few of the Germans fired up at it. As the plane banked upwards and turned back towards the Channel, I heard cries from men lying in the street. Some of them were bleeding and a few lay very still.

"By our own side!" one man wailed. "Killed by our own bloody side!" I felt like wailing too.

We lay there for a few minutes, utterly dejected, until some trucks pulled in and we began helping to load the wounded and the dead into them. Then we were marched into a walled courtyard in front of the village school.

"Für euch ist der Krieg zu Ende," said the guard at the gate, repeating a phrase I'd heard several times already. Only then did I understand what it meant: "For you, the war is over."

If only, I thought. If only.

As I looked about the school playground, I recognized only a few men among the grimy, bloodied faces. I walked around looking for men from my platoon. There was no one. I knew that our lieutenant and sergeant were dead. And Turnbull and Smiler, too. But where were the rest of them? Where was Mackie? More than half of the men seemed to be from the Black Watch. What had happened to all the Royals? I could only hope that some of them had managed to swim out and be picked up by boats offshore. Perhaps a good number had made it through the barbed wire with Catto. Maybe they had joined up with the Essex Scottish and were now fighting in the town.

Then I heard the ringing voice of Sergeant-Major Murray. "Line up, men! Into formation! Show them we're soldiers!"

At the gate, I saw a group of Germans entering with an officer. We shuffled into line and squared our shoulders. Even some of the wounded tried to stand at attention — it made us feel less bedraggled and defeated. The German officer walked around, inspecting us. He was not at all the nasty Nazi of propaganda cartoons, and actually had a very quiet, calm manner. He looked at the wounds of a few of the men. As he walked out through the gate, Sergeant-Major Murray called out, "Company! At ease!"

Several German soldiers then arrived with pails of water and some pieces of black bread. I suddenly realized how hungry and parched I was. I gulped a mouthful of water and used some of it to wipe off my hands and face. Then I reached under my torn battle jacket to feel the wound on my side. It was very sore but was beginning to scab over. The left side of my chest was also tender and when I probed there it made me wince. I heard a rattle in my breast pocket. I reached in and pulled out the metal hand mirror that Mackie had given me. It had been punched inwards and looked like a tiny fist. Clasped inside its bent edges was a jagged piece of shrapnel that had been headed for my heart. Saved by the mirror! Thank you, Mackie, I thought.

Before long the gate was opened once again and to the sounds of *"Hände hoch!"* we were marched out of the schoolyard and up a winding hill out of Puys, our hands over our heads. We walked west on a road along the cliffs. As we came closer to Dieppe we could hear the sounds of gunfire. The deep booming sounds of heavy artillery were not far off — clearly the Rommel Battery had not been destroyed. With a sinking feeling, I thought about the men on the main Dieppe beaches and what murderous fire they must be facing. We could see planes wheeling in the blue sky overhead. As we descended into Dieppe, we caught a view of the beachfront covered with a heavy smokescreen. On the far headland stood the round turret of an old French castle and beyond it more chalk cliffs. My watch showed 1220 hours.

We crossed a bridge and walked under the steel cranes of the port of Dieppe. It sounded as if the gunfire was beginning to die down. We turned a corner and the beachfront and promenade lay in front of us. The firing on it seemed to have stopped.

As the grey smokescreen lifted we could see plumes of black smoke rising from shattered landing craft and burning tanks on the shore. The street in front of the promenade was lined with hotels and apartment blocks, many of them with scarred bricks and broken windows. Smoke was coming out of a large white building farther down the beachfront that I soon learned was the town's casino.

We were marched onto the concrete promenade that had once been a popular spot for day-trippers to stroll and eat ice cream. Now it held a few hundred bedraggled and battle-weary Canadian soldiers. A few of them were barefoot and bare-legged. I guessed that they had kicked off their boots and pants while trying to swim out to sea. Some of the wounded were being bandaged by German medics.

I walked among the huddled knots of men, looking for Mackie and any of my platoon-mates.

"We never had a chance!" I heard an angry voice say.

"Who planned this cock-up?" muttered another.

"The damn Brits!" said a third man. "Where was the Navy? Those destroyers were supposed to give us cover — their guns were like bloody popguns!"

I nodded in agreement. I'd seen one destroyer fire onto Blue Beach from offshore. All it did was knock off a chunk of cliff that fell onto the men below.

Then with a loud roar another Spitfire swooped down over us. Once again we scattered and dived for the pavement. We heard the *rat-tat-tat* of automatic fire, but luckily it didn't hit any of us. A man lying near me rolled over and shook his fist. "Where were you when we needed you?" he screamed at the departing plane.

After we stood up, I saw that groups of men were being marched off the promenade. When our turn came, we walked by the beach and I caught a glimpse of bodies and a severed leg bobbing in the bloody surf. It made me want to vomit. For what? I thought. All these man sacrificed . . . and for what?

Then we passed two Churchill tanks that had been abandoned on the promenade. I noted that it was surrounded by concrete barriers. These tanks could have done nothing except roar around the promenade.

Shouldn't somebody have known this? I thought. We climbed over the barriers and walked with our hands on our heads through the streets of Dieppe. Some of the townspeople looked at us sullenly but others flashed the V for Victory symbol with their fingers. A Jerry photographer was snapping photographs of us. I could only imagine how the German newspapers would crow over our defeat.

Before long we were herded into the walled grounds of the Dieppe hospital. Men lay on stretchers near the doors. French nuns and some doctors were tending to them, clearly over-whelmed by the number of wounded. Trucks soon arrived to take some of the injured to other hospitals. As we squatted on the grass, the guards came and demanded that we empty our pock-ets. We grumbled at this, but I eventually tossed my paybook and watch onto a pile that included wallets, fountain pens, rings, pocket knives and tobacco pouches. A young fellow from Montreal threw a grenade onto the pile. The guards all dived for cover, until they heard us laughing and realized that the pin on the grenade hadn't been pulled.

By late afternoon, all those who could walk were formed up into a long column outside the hospital. By my estimate there were about sixteen hundred of us. Some of the men had blankets around their shoulders. Many had no pants. A few of those without shoes had wrapped their feet in bits of cloth. Slowly we marched forward with our hands on our heads. Some of the townspeople tried to pass bottles of water or wine to us, but the guards pushed them away with bayonets.

As we crossed over the bridge into the docklands I saw a small group of our soldiers approaching. Men ahead of me were calling out greetings to them. As they drew closer I recognized Lt-Colonel Catto walking with his hands up. There were about a dozen men behind him, one of them walking with his arms around the shoulders of two others. When he lifted his head, I saw that it was Mackie.

"Mack, Mack!" I shouted. "Are you okay?"

"Hey, Allie!" he replied, grinning, his white teeth lighting up his grimy face. "I'm fine. Nothin' big. Just a bullet to the foot. But it went right through!" he said, raising his wounded foot.

I pulled out the crumpled mirror and waved it. "The mirror saved me, Mack!" I called out, but he had already passed by. He craned his head back and I shook the mirror like a rattle until I felt a sharp prod in my backside.

"*Komm!*" growled a guard. I hopped back into line. I was now farther back than when I'd spotted Mackie. Around me were a group of men from the Fusiliers Mont-Royal. One of the FMRs started singing the *"Marseillaise"* in a high clear voice.

"*Allons enfants de la Patrie,*" he began and a

chorus of FMRs joined in. I sang along as well, summoning a memory of Miss Carlton, my Grade Ten French teacher, teaching us the words. This was a scene she could never have imagined, I thought.

An old French man saluted us, and others standing by the roadside sang along with tears in their eyes. It had been over two years since they had heard their national anthem. The guards tried to stop the singing but we ignored them.

On the outskirts of Dieppe a farmer brought out a metal milk container and started ladling it out to us, but one of the guards kicked it over and shoved him away.

Then an old woman pushing a wheelbarrow of tomatoes had a better idea. She picked up a ripe tomato and began cursing us. *"Crétins! Imbéciles!"* she yelled hoarsely. Then she began hurling the tomatoes at us. Some of the men caught them and put them in their pockets to eat later. I saw two guards roaring with laughter and one patted her on the shoulder. She smiled back, very pleased at having fooled the Germans.

Soon we were in open countryside. I looked out at the fields of yellow wheat glowing in the evening sunshine. I heard birds singing in the trees. A wave of euphoria swept over me. I was alive!

Mackie was alive! I had never felt so alive in my whole life. Alive! The word kept repeating in my brain with every step, a-*live,* a-*live,* a-*live.*

A barefoot soldier abruptly ended my reverie. He had fallen back in the line because gravel from the road was digging into his blistered feet. I kneeled and helped him pluck out the gravel and then put his arm around my shoulder. As he limped along beside me, I learned that his name was Stan Darch, one of the Rileys from Hamilton. He said that his platoon had managed to get inside the casino on the beachfront and clear the Germans out of it. "But we couldn't get into the town," he continued. "There was no way. They were firing down on us somethin' wicked."

"For us, too, it was murder," said one of the FMRs in accented English. "We were supposed to be the reserves. But the commanders — they had no clue what was really happening. So they sent us in. But when we got through the smoke, we were just pinned down on the beach. You moved and you got it!"

We passed a road sign that said that Envermeu was just 3 kilometres ahead. "Envermeu," I said to Stan. "Let's hope we're stopping there for the night."

"Oh sure," said Stan, "they'll be getting the best hotel ready for us."

As we came down a hill towards Envermeu, we were greeted by an amazing site. It was like something out of a dream. Approaching us was a bride in a long white dress carrying a bouquet of flowers. Beside her was the groom in a tuxedo with satin lapels. The rest of the gaily-dressed wedding party walked behind. They had all just come from a wedding in the village church, whose tower we could see through the trees. As they waited for us to pass, we called out greetings and congratulations. Some of the guys had English coins in their pockets and tossed them to the bride. "Here, honey," I heard someone say, "buy yourself a wedding present!"

As Stan and I drew near, some of the wedding guests looked down at his bleeding feet with pity. Suddenly I saw a young man with a flower in his buttonhole — I think he was the best man — bend down. He unlaced his shiny new shoes and handed them to Stan. Stan was stunned and began to say, "No, no I couldn't," but the guards suddenly grabbed the best man and hustled him away in his stocking feet. Stan immediately squatted down in the road and put on the shoes. As he was lacing them up a guard came and booted him in the backside. But Stan didn't care — when he caught up with me he had a huge smile on his face. "Hope they don't give that guy any grief," he said. "That was one fine thing, what he done."

We walked into the village of Envermeu and stopped in front of the church where the wedding had just taken place. The officers were separated out and I saw Lt-Colonel Catto and the others climb the steps of the church, where they were to spend the night. There were groans and muttered protests as the rest of us were marched out of the village. We walked for a few miles more until we were herded inside an abandoned brick factory. It was just a shell of a building with a dirt floor, no toilets and only one water pipe outside. We milled about, complaining loudly, sometimes tripping over the wounded. Many of them had fallen down from sheer exhaustion.

Suddenly there was a shrill whistle and a loud English voice shouted, "Atten-shun! Silence, please!"

A short man stood very straight atop a pile of bricks. "I am Regimental Sergeant-Major Beesley of the British Number Three Commando Group," he announced. "We *must* have some order here. We are soldiers and we must conduct ourselves as soldiers. The enemy must *not* see us as cowardly in defeat. Everyone here fought bravely under impossible conditions. We were defeated through no fault of our own."

A few lame cheers went up. But I could see some of the guys rolling their eyes as if to say, "Who is this Limey telling us what to do?" Beesley then ordered that one corner of the old factory floor be cleared for the wounded. When they had been moved and settled there, he organized a group of men to carry water to them in their helmets. Later, when some loaves of black bread were brought in, Beesley directed some of the other sergeants to break up and distribute the small portions of bread evenly and fairly. Finally he delivered a small pep talk on how we could survive as prisoners of war. He concluded by saying, "Make your enemy respect you. In time they will fear you!"

I found it hard to believe that the Germans would ever fear me. But I had changed my mind about Beesley and was glad that he had taken charge. He seemed a natural leader and we needed someone like him.

It was now dark outside and I felt utterly spent. Could it only have been this morning that we were crouched in our landing craft off Blue Beach? It seemed a lifetime ago. I balled up my battle jacket and lay down near a dusty wall.

Within minutes I sank into a welcome oblivion.

CHAPTER 11
JOURNEY INTO CAPTIVITY
August 20, 1942, 0300 hours

The oblivion didn't last long. I woke up in the dark, aching all over. The dirt floor was hard and my side and chest were throbbing. I ran my fingers over the cut on my side and felt some pus oozing out of it. Great, I thought, it's infected.

Then I heard moans from the corner where the wounded were lying and felt guilty for even worrying about a cut. I could also hear muffled sobs coming from a few of the men around me. For some reason, an image of Lieutenant Whitman flashed into my brain and I began to cry as well. Why am I weeping for a man I never liked? I wondered. Even more tears flowed as I remembered how I'd made fun of him and called him Twitman. He had a family and friends back home, who would soon learn that they'd never see him again. Why him and not me? Why Hartley and Smiler and Turnbull and almost all of our platoon and not me? They were better soldiers — hell, they were better *men* — than me.

It was almost a relief when grey morning light began seeping into our dusty compound. The guards roused us with barked orders, water was brought in, and small hunks of black bread were passed around. Just after sunrise we once again formed up into a long column on the country road. I noticed that some of the barefoot men now wore odd-looking shoes that had been cut out of army life jackets. A sergeant from the FMRs had stayed up all night making these. A man near me who was wearing these ungainly shoes — Norm, from the Essex Scottish — was also dragging his wounded leg. I offered my shoulder as support. As we trudged along I told him that I thought I might be one of the few men from my platoon who hadn't been killed or wounded.

"I heard the Royals were hit harder than any other regiment," he replied.

I told him about some of the guilty feelings I'd been having.

"Guilty?" Norm replied, looking straight at me. "There's nothing to be guilty about! We all did the best we could. It's the idiots who planned this thing who should feel guilty. You should feel lucky! Lucky, and, well, grateful . . . yeah, grateful."

As we passed the gates to a farm, two little girls ran out and gave us the V for Victory salute and then ran away. We smiled and, all of a sudden, I did feel grateful. Grateful for men like Norm. Grateful for the morning sunshine that warmed my face. Grateful for still having a life when so many others had lost theirs.

By the afternoon, however, the sun that I'd enjoyed in the early morning was beating down relentlessly. We'd been slogging along in humid heat for hours with hardly a break, and with no food and very little water. Norm's face was red and his leg was oozing pus. I felt his forehead and realized he had a high fever. Another man came and took Norm's other arm over his shoulder.

Late in the afternoon, we saw a sign that said Paris was only 25 kilometres away. I've always wanted to go to Paris, I thought, just not in this way. Only a few kilometres later, near a village called Verneulles, we suddenly caught sight of our destination. It was a large barbed-wire enclosure with some shabby grey barracks inside. As we approached the gates, everyone fell silent. Just inside them was the grim silhouette of a large wooden gallows.

"Looks like they're planning a necktie party," quipped a fellow from the Calgary Tanks. Nobody laughed. We had heard about Nazi executions of enemy soldiers.

Once we were inside the gates, I took Norm to a long line of wounded that had formed outside the infirmary. I sat him down in the line and the guards gestured me towards another long grey hut. When I walked inside, it was already crowded. There were no beds, so some men were stretched out on the floor. There were no blankets either.

"I guess the management wasn't expecting so many guests," said Fred, another fellow from the Rileys, but nobody even smiled.

Two guards came in a little later with a bucket of cabbage soup and a few loaves of black bread. We had no eating utensils so some guys drank out of a tin helmet. One or two used an army boot. A man near me had found an old tin can and I waited till he was done, and borrowed it. The watery soup had a greasy taste and there was sand at the bottom of the bucket. I nibbled slowly on my scrap of black bread, trying to get rid of the taste of the soup. A restless sleep on the hard floor followed. Three men in our hut died during the night.

The next morning we received another bucket of watery soup with a hunk of black bread, and the same again in the evening. Everyone was starving. Around mid-morning I'd seen Norm sitting in the line outside the infirmary. He had received some disinfectant and a paper bandage for his leg, but was still waiting to see a doctor. When I spoke to him he was quite calm and said that three of the Canadian medical officers and one German doctor were working around the clock. "They'll get to me," he said calmly. I managed to get some disinfectant and a paper bandage for the cut on my side and by the next day it had dried up.

Then Mackie arrived, hopping into camp on one foot. He had been sent to the hospital in Rouen for treatment and shipped to Verneulles by train with some other wounded men.

I've never been so happy to see anyone in my life. I ran towards him and we hugged. I cried quite unashamedly and so did he.

"I'm so sorry, Allie. This is my fault," he said hoarsely. "I got you into this."

"No, no," I replied. "Wasn't you who planned this thing, it was some idiot Brits!"

We both laughed and Mackie showed me the bullet that had gone through his foot and ended up in his boot. He'd saved it as a souvenir. I then pulled out the punched-in mirror with the shrapnel in it.

"Is *that* what that is?" he said, grinning. "I wondered what the heck it was that you were waving at me." Then he glanced towards a man waiting next to him who had a badly mangled arm. "Listen,

Allie," he said, "we'll talk more later. I gotta get old Cec here to see a doc."

Cec Towler had been in the bed beside Mackie's in the Rouen hospital. The evening before they left, some doctors had walked through the wards deciding who would stay and who would leave. Mackie was told he was leaving but Cec was ordered to stay. Then Cec overheard that his arm was to be amputated the following day. Early the next morning, with Mackie's help, he had slipped out of bed, joined the lineup of walking wounded outside the hospital and managed to get on the train undetected.

I was able to find room for Mackie in the same hut that I was in. Scrounging around, I found some old sacks and made a pillow to raise his foot. He told me not to fuss and said that no major bones had been broken in his foot and that it was healing nicely.

Over time, he told me what had happened to him on Blue Beach. During the firing on our landing craft he had jumped over the side into deep water. His Bren gun had fallen to the bottom and he'd had to scramble to retrieve it. Wading forward, he too had found Smiler leaning against the boat. Mackie had tried to drag him onto the shore, but the pain was too much and Smiler begged Mackie to just leave him.

Mackie then saw Hartley lying on the beach and flopped down beside him. He tried to get his Bren gun firing, but it had jammed from being in salt water. When Hartley saw the men of the second wave arriving, he sent Mackie to join them. Mackie sprinted down the beach, scooping up a Tommy gun from a dead man on the way. He then spied Catto leading a small party of men in a dash towards the seawall, and decided to follow. At the wall, he'd helped boost up two men trying to hack away at the barbed wire.

He described with awe how an enraged lieutenant named Stewart had climbed onto the seawall to provide cover. "He just stood there blasting away with his Bren gun. How he didn't get picked off, I'll never know," Mackie said. "He kept hollering for more ammo so I scrambled around picking up Bren mags on the beach and throwing them up to him. He got hit in the legs but he just stood there cursing and firing."

Mackie was one of the last to shinny up the seawall and crawl through the wire. As he did so, a bullet ricocheted off the wall into his foot. He managed to pull himself through the wire and limp up through the gully. Ahead, he could hear shouts and gunfire. Germans in a machine-gun nest were firing from inside one of the holiday cottages on the cliff. Mackie joined the other men taking cover around it. A lieutenant named Ryerson and two other men charged at the cottage with their Sten guns and killed three Germans. They then ran to flush out other cliff houses — only to find them empty.

Lieutenant Ryerson was then sent to check out the road to Puys, but he soon returned to report that a German patrol was headed towards them. Catto quickly led his twenty or so men west towards Dieppe, hoping to link up with the Essex Scottish on the eastern headland as planned. But when they approached the Rommel Battery they could hear its big guns firing on the beach below. Catto knew he didn't have the men or the firepower to attack the battery, so they took cover in some nearby woods and waited — that's when Mackie had a minute to inspect his bleeding foot and found the bullet inside his boot. When they saw the rest of the Royals marching by with their hands up, Catto knew it was hopeless. With no chance of escape, they surrendered later in the afternoon.

Other men in the camp at Verneulles also told stories of what had happened to them at Dieppe. It helped pass the time during our miserable days there.

By the third day we were so hungry that some

men were gathering weeds and grass and putting it into the soup for extra nourishment.

That evening a soldier from the FMRs came over to Mackie and me. *"Pour vous,"* he said, handing us a can of processed meat and two apples. We both looked at him with stunned expressions.

"Nous sommes tous canadiens. Nous avons bien combattu ensemble," he said.

"Merci, mon ami!" was the best reply I could manage in my high-school French. But I understood what he had said and related it to Mackie.

"Canadians who fought well together," he repeated. "Yep, that's us!"

We later found out that French officials who had collaborated with the Nazis had brought extra rations to the camp for the French-speaking prisoners. They considered them to be French rather than Canadians. The Germans thought it would be a good way of sowing discord among us. The FMRs accepted the rations, but decided to share them with all the other prisoners.

I've never eaten an apple that tasted as good.

On the fifth day, we were marched out of the camp to the train station in Verneulles. There we were given a loaf of black bread each and a small can of liverwurst to share with two or three others.

"Ten will be shot for every man who escapes,"

bellowed a German officer as we were herded towards the wooden boxcars.

"Aww, they're just bluffing," whispered Mackie, as he limped beside me with his arm around my shoulder.

I wasn't so sure about that.

German soldiers prodded us with bayonets and cries of *"Schnell! Schnell!"* as we were hurried towards the train along with hundreds of other prisoners. I could see *CHURCHILL'S 2nd FRONT KAPUTT!* chalked in bold letters on the side of one boxcar. As we got closer, I could also see *GANGSTERSCHWEIN* — gangster pigs — and other insults. Further down, neatly stencilled in French on each boxcar, were the words *40 hommes, 8 chevaux*.

"Great," I said to Mackie. "These are supposed to be for forty men or eight horses!"

When we crawled into a boxcar we discovered that there were at least fifty of us. With some of the wounded lying in stretchers, we were crowded in so tightly that we could only stand or crouch. On the floor was filthy straw matted with cattle droppings. Straw was also floating in the milk can that held our drinking water and in the wooden pail that was to be our toilet. The stench was already bad enough. In the August heat I knew it was sure to get worse.

The only source of fresh air was a small square opening with steel bars across it and barbed wire on the outside. Mackie and I tried to edge our way towards it. After the train lurched forward we soon felt a tiny breeze coming through it.

"I'll bet we could pry the bars off that window," said Mackie.

"Sure, just like Superman," I replied.

We had been told during training that it was the duty of every prisoner of war to try to escape. But leaping from a moving train didn't seem like a sensible idea to me.

"There's no way I'm gonna be their prisoner," said Mackie. "The war could go on for years!"

"You're right, mate," said a British commando squatting nearby. "They're taking us to Germany. Our best chance is to escape now, while we're still in France."

Mackie crawled over to him and I could over-hear them making eager plans. Most of the soldiers near us were French-speaking FMRs, who may not have been aware of what was being planned. Just as well, I thought, since Mackie and his new friend could get us all shot.

As darkness fell, a couple of other English commandos began pulling hard at the bars on the window. To my amazement, they managed to pry them slightly apart. Soon they were reaching out and pulling down the barbed wire outside.

"I'm going with them, Allie," Mackie said as he came back beside me.

"Mackie, you *can't!* The Jerries'll shoot you!" I whispered.

"Naww, they won't," he replied.

"But you can't speak French," I said. "And what about your foot? You going to *hobble* across France?"

One of the commandos came over and told Mackie that there was a small fellow who thought he could just squeeze through the bars. It wasn't long before I saw the head and shoulders of this man disappearing through the window. In his bare feet he clung with his fingers and toes to the side of the rocking boxcar, slowly edging his way along it. Minutes of silence passed. Then we heard a rap at the sliding door. Several prisoners pushed the door open and the short man fell into the car with a huge grin on his face. He had managed to twist off the lock with a piece of pipe he had picked up at the train station and hidden in his pants. The courage of this small, brave soldier bucked up my own.

"If you're going, I'm going first," I hissed to Mackie. "Someone's gotta catch you!"

We crawled closer to the partly opened door. Looking out, I could see a wheat field illuminated by moonlight. My first thought was just how beautiful it was. Then I quickly saw how little cover it would provide. My heart began pounding like mad. For the second time in a week I realized that very soon I might be killed. The Germans had a machine gunner on the roof of every second boxcar. Our side of the train was now in shadow, but once we jumped we would be easy targets.

The door was pushed open a little wider and one man soon had his legs outside with his feet dangling just above the railway ties. Mackie and I edged closer to the door. I silently prepared to do a forward roll into the field with my arms folded. My plan was to grab Mackie when he landed and pull him into whatever cover I could find.

"Stay in the car! You'll get us all shot!" rang out a deep voice in the darkness. Other men called out, "No, no, let's go!" and began lacing up their boots.

The train slowed as it started to go into a curve. Within minutes our open door would be easily seen from the roof. Suddenly we heard a yell followed by the loud *rat-tat-tat* of machine-gun fire. The man in the doorway flipped back inward on top of us. The door behind him was quickly slammed shut.

I lay with my back pressed against the boxcar wall with my heart thudding. There was no chance of escape from our car now. The Germans would see to that. But I was alive! Mackie was alive! Prison camp might be hell, but we could survive it. I suddenly felt a wild joy flooding through me. I loved the small shaft of moonlight I could see through the pried-open bars. I loved the clacking rhythm of the train as I silently whispered in time to it, "A-*live* . . . a-*live* . . . a-*live* . . ."

CHAPTER 12
STALAG VIIIB
August 30, 1942, 1200 hours

With a groan and several sharp squeals the train gradually came to a stop. I heard the slamming noises of boxcar doors being opened. Was this it? Were we there? After five days packed into a stinking boxcar, I was almost beyond caring. Then our latch was unlocked and sunlight flooded the filthy floor.

"Aufstehen!" shouted a guard.

Blinking our eyes in the blinding light, and desperately weak from hunger, we slowly began to get to our feet.

"Raus! Raus! Schnell!" yelled another guard even more loudly, motioning us out of the boxcar.

"Get the wounded out first!" said a voice near me. Several men began to move the four soldiers on stretchers towards the door. The journey had been hardest on them — they should have been in hospital beds with clean sheets, not in this dark and dirty boxcar. One of them was very pale and barely moving.

On the platform there was a sign that read *LAMSDORF*. My heart sank. An English commando in our boxcar had said that we were probably headed for Stalag VIIIB near Lamsdorf. He said it was the largest enemy POW camp, deep inside Germany near the Czech border. On the track opposite, prisoners in rags were unloading sacks from a train. My heart sank even further — they looked like bearded skeletons. Then I saw a guard raise his bullwhip and strike one of them.

Was this what awaited us?

"They're Russians," I heard one of the commandos behind me say. "The Jerries use them as slave labour."

"They whip me and they're dead," muttered one of the Royals.

In front of the station, Sergeant-Major Beesley was organizing men to carry the wounded. He ignored the shouts of the guards and ordered us to form up in a column behind the stretchers. As we walked along the road out of the village we soon saw cherry trees laden with ripe fruit. My mouth actually watered. But the guards immediately pointed at the trees with their rifles and then at us, indicating that anyone who tried to pick the cherries would be shot.

As the guard towers of Stalag VIIIB came into view, Beesley stopped the column and ordered us into marching formation with three men abreast. Then, in his best parade-ground voice, he called out, "Company! By the left! Quick . . . march!" With shoulders squared we marched forward, swinging our arms in unison. Some of us were without shoes or pants. Some, like Mackie, were limping, or like Norm, struggling forward on makeshift crutches. But we marched proudly with our heads lifted high. The guards looked befuddled — this was not how defeated men should behave!

Then we heard a roaring sound, like you hear in a baseball stadium after a home run. As we drew nearer the camp we saw hundreds and hundreds of British prisoners standing behind the wire fence, waving and cheering and whooping. As we approached the camp's main gate, the men at the front of the column started singing our version of an old First World War army song.

Canucks are coming, Canucks are coming
There's drum, drum, drumming everywhere!

The British prisoners shouted their approval. "Good old Canada!" several called out. I later found out that most of them had been in prison camp since June of 1940 when Hitler's armies had overrun France and trapped the British forces on the French coast at a town called Dunkirk. Boats had raced across the Channel and rescued thousands of British soldiers there. But these men had not escaped and had now spent over two years in prison camp. They were excited to see us. The very fact that an attack had been mounted on Hitler's Europe gave them hope.

The Germans would soon do their best to dampen our defiant spirit. Inside the main gate we were lined up for hours in the hot afternoon sun. First we were searched and counted. And recounted. Then we were photographed and given a brown disk with our *Kriegsgefangener* number on it. My war prisoner number was 26216. Then we were marched through a second gate and counted again.

Two high barbed-wire fences surrounded the camp. Rolls of fiercely spiked wire filled the two-yard space between them. Inside the second fence was a knee-high wire called a trip wire. We were told that anyone stepping over it could be shot without warning. Guards in machine-gun towers scanned the camp constantly. My heart sank at the thought of anyone trying to escape from a place like this.

After hours in the hot sun with no food, some of the men were starting to fall down. Mackie began to wobble on his one good foot so I grabbed him by the elbow. Eventually the wounded on stretchers were carried off to the infirmary, accompanied by our three medical officers. Then a group of British prisoners approached the barbed wire. They spoke to the guards and the gate was opened. As they came towards us we saw they were carrying pails of soup — their lunch ration — to give to us. It was the same kind of weak and smelly cabbage soup we had been given at Verneulles and it had grubs and sand in it. But to starving men it was life-giving. There were no spoons so I drank my soup from a boot.

After our meagre meal the third gate was opened and we walked past the British prisoners' long wooden barracks to a wired-off compound at the back of the camp. Another gate was opened. In front of us stood four low, wide, wooden barracks with small windows and a door at each end. Each one had a washroom in the middle and two living areas called huts on either side. I was glad that Mackie and I were assigned to the same hut, Number 19B. On the other side of the washroom was 19A. Three other barracks were behind ours, and behind the last one was the Forty Holer, the latrine for our entire compound. Each hut slept about sixty people. Once we got inside 19B, men were quickly claiming beds in the three-tier wooden bunks that ran along one wall.

"Go grab us a coupla bunks," said Mackie, who was limping badly.

I elbowed my way down the room and stood beside a tier of bunks. There were no mattresses — only a few wooden slats on the bottom of each bed.

"Hey, what're we gonna sleep on?" someone called out.

"You gotta fill your own palliasses!" said Bill Lee, the sergeant in charge of our hut. "There's bags and straw outside on the parade ground."

I left Mackie by the two bunks we'd claimed and went out to the parade ground — an area of pounded earth and weeds at the front of the compound. I took two burlap bags and filled each one with straw.

"Gee, this stuff's actually clean!" I heard some-one say.

This was a relief. The filthy straw in the train cars had been so full of fleas we were all scratching from flea bites. I took the two palliasses inside to where Mackie was standing. I wanted him to take the lower bunk because of his foot, but he waved me aside and hopped up to the second one. His palliasse sagged down through the slats to just above my face. Soon a large guy from the South Saskatchewan Regiment came and dragged his palliasse up to the top bunk.

Mackie and I were both exhausted and closed

our eyes, but there were too many men moving about for sleep to be possible.

"I'd kill for a hot shower," Mackie said.

"I heard some of the guys got soap from the Brits," said the deep voice of Big Jim, the Saskatchewaner on the top bunk.

I got up and went into the washroom. It was a bare room with a long tin trough in the centre with about twelve cold-water taps above it. In front of each tap was a naked man washing himself. I went back and helped Mackie down from his bunk and we joined the line by the trough. Because there were only a couple of bars of soap to go around, we had to make the most of them. When our turn came we dumped our socks, shirt and underpants into the tin trough. We shoved our heads under the spigot, soaped up our hair and passed the bar of soap to the next guy. With the suds from our hair we soaped our bodies, using our shirts as washcloths. Then the leftover suds in the trough were used to wash our socks and underwear and shirts. We attacked our ten days' growth — Mackie had grown a full black beard; mine was just reddish and patchy — with an old safety razor borrowed from the British compound. We then hung our clothes to dry over the ends of our bunks. I wrapped myself in the one coarse grey blanket each of us had been given and crawled onto the rustling palliasse.

"Being clean has never felt so good!" I said to Mackie. But from above, I only heard deep breathing and a few contented snores.

* * *

"Achtung! Alle Männer nach draussen zum Appell!"

The harsh voice on the loudspeaker kept repeating the word *Appell*. I ignored it, as I was dreaming that I was in bed at home and my mother was playing the radio too loudly downstairs. When I finally opened my eyes I saw that a few men were climbing down from their bunks. We didn't know exactly what *Appell* meant, though we were about to find out. Suddenly the door to 19B was flung open and two guards burst in, followed by a short, uniformed man with a high, whining voice.

"Raus! Raus!" he yelled as he stormed past our bunks and herded us outside. We figured that *Appell* must mean roll call. Sure enough, he motioned to the guards to jab anyone still in bed with their rifle butts.

This was our introduction to Spitfire, the chief guard or *Blockführer* of the compound. His face had a permanent snarl on it and every time he opened his mouth he seemed to "spit fire." So the name just stuck. As we gathered on the parade ground, Spitfire kept shouting, *"Alle in Fünferreihen!"* We couldn't understand him so we ignored him. Other guards held up five fingers, indicating they wanted us in groups of five. We ignored them too.

"All right, men," Beesley finally called out. "Line up in rows of five!" We shuffled into formation.

Spitfire was sulky that we had obeyed Beesley's orders but not his. He began counting us but took his time doing it. He would pretend to lose count and then start again. At one point he wandered off and kept us standing there. Then he came back and began counting us from the start.

"Isn't he the little Napoleon!" I heard an English voice mutter.

"Little twerp, is more like it," a Canadian responded.

That first morning, roll call took well over an hour. Sometimes on freezing winter days, Spitfire would keep us standing there even longer, if he felt like it.

Each day the routine was the same. The loudspeakers in the yard would summon us to the parade ground. After *Appell* was over, two men from each hut would go to the cookhouse outside our compound and bring back *Kübels* of mint tea. A *Kübel* looked just like a large, metal garbage can and was carried with two poles shoved through the handles. In the morning it was usually filled with a greenish liquid we called mint tea, even though there wasn't much mint in it. Some days we got fake coffee made from burnt barley that was equally vile. Most of the guys used the fake tea for shaving as there was no other hot water. We also got our daily ration of black bread — one loaf to be shared among ten men. Since all knives had been confiscated, cutting the bread posed a challenge. But a fellow from the Calgary Tanks managed to sharpen up an old door hinge and became expert at slicing a piece of bread exactly three-quarters of an inch thick. For starving men, every crumb counted. Sometimes we were given fake jam made from beet pulp that looked and tasted like pink glue. On Sundays we would sometimes get a slice of liverwurst or a piece of fishy-smelling cheese.

At midday the *Kübel*s would be brought in again, this time either filled with watery soup or boiled potatoes. If it was potatoes each man received two small potatoes or one medium-sized one. And that would be all the food we would get for the rest of the day. In the evening there would be another *Appell* before dark and we would then go to bed hungry. I was hungry all the time. I thought about food constantly

— about my mother's Sunday roast, about beans on toast, about hot scones with cream and jam.

Hunger was one of the constants of POW life, but boredom was another. Each boring day seemed just like the boring day before. Mackie spent most of his time playing cards. He was a good bridge and poker player and often had little piles of cigarettes beside him — proof of his winnings. Cigarettes were what we used for money. You could trade with them and sometimes even use them to bribe the "goons" — our name for the guards.

But I wasn't a card player — what I really longed for was a book. I went to the wire of the British compound one day with some cigarettes Mackie had given me, hoping to trade them for something to read. But there were no books to be had. I was told that some soldiers occasionally received books in the mail from England but that they were soon used for toilet paper. Having become accustomed to using my hand for that purpose — and then rubbing it in the sandy soil of the parade ground — I could understand the allure of paper.

* * *

A few days after we had arrived at Stalag VIIIB, Harry Beesley reminded us that it was the duty of every POW to try to escape. The idea of digging an escape tunnel got everyone excited, particularly Mackie. Our hut was chosen as the entrance for a tunnel, since it was the closest to the wire fence. Bill Lee was one of the Royal Canadian Engineers and thus a good person to take charge of a tunnelling operation. In mid-September he and Sid Cleasby, a burly miner from Timmins, had begun to cut a square in the concrete floor under a bunk near the wall. They used a saw that had been carefully crafted from some pilfered sheet metal. After the concrete slab was cut and lifted up, we took turns digging out the earth underneath with tools made from tin cans. Lookouts were posted at the doors and windows to keep an eye out for goons. Any trace of earth would have given the game away, so we scooped it into homemade bags that we dumped down the Forty Holer at night. If the Russian prisoners who had the nasty job of shovelling out the "honey pit" beneath the latrine ever noticed the extra earth, they didn't let on to the Germans.

During our third week in the camp, a stack of brown cardboard boxes was spotted at the gate. The word spread like wildfire — the Red Cross parcels were here! We gathered near the wire, almost crazed with excitement. Real food at last! Beesley elbowed his way through us and took charge of the transfer of the boxes. He announced that instead of the one box per soldier as the Red Cross had intended, we had only received one box for every four men. We all groaned, but knew that we'd manage to share a box with our fellow "muckers." During our first week in the camp we'd divided up into muckers' groups of four or six men with whom we shared all the food we could find or scrounge. I think we got the name from the English expression "mucking in," for making do. Mackie and I were in a muckers' group with Big Jim from the top bunk and a fellow named Wilf, one of the Camerons from Winnipeg.

The four of us sat on my bunk and carefully opened the Red Cross box. No parcel we'd received as kids on Christmas morning was ever as eagerly anticipated. We pulled out a large can of Klim powdered milk. Then a can of butter, a tin of sugar, a packet of tea, raisins, powdered eggs, biscuits, cans of sardines, cocoa powder, pudding and canned vegetables. There was also a bar of soap, a large bar of chocolate and a can of fifty cigarettes. Since none of us were smokers, this gave each of us a little extra currency. We weren't tea drinkers either so we immediately swapped our tea for some cocoa powder. Everything was divided up fairly among the four of us. I stowed my stash under my bunk. I never had to worry about theft — the POW code of honour meant you never stole another man's food no matter how hungry you were.

Nothing in the Red Cross parcel was wasted. Wilf could put a wire handle on a sardine can and make it into a soup bowl, or turn a taller can into a handy mug. And we used the empty cardboard boxes to get rid of the sandy soil from the tunnel. As we walked around the compound we would let it leak out from the boxes and then scuff it in with our boots. When the goons saw us with the boxes they figured we were simply guarding our food or doing a little bartering.

* * *

The evenings after the Red Cross parcels arrived were always the best ones we had. That first night, I remember sipping hot cocoa and chatting with one of the FMRs who was helping me improve my high-school French. I looked over at the smoky poker circle surrounding Mackie and saw from the pile of cigarettes at his elbow that he was having a winning night. My full stomach filled me with a feeling of contentment.

But evenings like this one were rare. And very soon, misery would come calling, in a way that we could never have imagined.

CHAPTER 13
ROPES AND CHAINS
October 8, 1942

At *Appell* that morning we knew something was up. The barbed wire around our compound was surrounded by German soldiers holding machine guns. Several armoured cars stood outside on the roadway with their guns pointed right at us. Had someone ratted on us about the tunnel?

We lined up in our usual rows of five. Then we saw the commandant of the camp arrive at our gate. The morning sun reflected off his perfectly shined boots, and on his cap I could see a Nazi eagle clasping a swastika. As he entered, Beesley crisply called us to attention.

With a stony face, the commandant pulled out an official-looking document. He handed it to an interpreter who proceeded to read it aloud to us in halting English: "The German government has always shown the utmost clemency to prisoners of war and accorded them the treatment due to honourable men captured in battle."

"Baloney!" someone behind me called out. A few others jeered.

The interpreter waited for the noise to die down and then continued. "After the abortive enemy invasion at Dieppe, many German soldiers were found shot with their hands tied behind their backs."

A nervous murmur rippled through our ranks. There was just no way this was true.

The interpreter went on. "The German government has demanded an apology from the British government and an assurance that such inhumane treatment will be discontinued in future. The British government has refused to apologize and therefore the German government has no choice but to take reprisals against all members of the Dieppe Force."

Reprisals! This word was greeted with icy silence. We knew about German reprisals. Only a few months ago an entire Czech village had been massacred as revenge for the assassination of one Nazi official. I felt my heart begin to hammer in my chest. The soldiers at the wire raised their guns menacingly. Beesley was ordered to march the first ten men into a nearby barracks. The POWs from our hut, 19B, were the first group in line.

Beesley swung about and spoke to us in a calm voice. "Men," he said, "I don't know what's going to happen. But whatever it is, we're going to act like soldiers. First two rows, right turn!"

Bill Lee led off the first ten men. They marched smartly with their arms swinging high. One of them began whistling "The Maple Leaf Forever" and the others joined in. Mackie and I were now in the front row. Would they only shoot the first ten, I wondered? Or would we be next? We waited for the sound of gunshots. I closed my eyes and thought of my mother. I could hear my ragged breathing. But there were no sounds of firing. I opened my eyes.

"Second two rows, right turn!" came the order. I glanced at Mackie, who gave me a wink. We, too, whistled as we marched into the barracks, but a little shakily. Inside, we saw a row of German soldiers standing with ropes over their shoulders. Were they planning to *beat* us, I wondered? Then an officer stepped forward and called us all *Gangsterschwein*. He took a rope and motioned to one of his men to hold up his hands, then demonstrated how our wrists would be tied in front of us. "Till Church-eel apologize!" he added in English.

"And Hell freezes over!" someone called out. We laughed nervously and the officer shouted at us to be quiet. But I felt relief flooding through me. We weren't going to be shot! They were just going to tie our hands! I looked at Mackie, who shrugged and rolled his eyes. In turn, each of us stepped forward and held up our wrists while they were roughly tied. As we were shoved out the back door we were almost giddy with relief. Once back in our hut we began working to loosen the ropes.

But it wasn't long before the grim reality of being tied up sank in. Simple tasks like cutting a slice of bread or spooning soup into your mouth became difficult. Going to the latrine was the worst of all. Men who had been stretcher-bearers were appointed to be *Sanitäters*, as the goons called them. We would have to go to the Forty Holer in groups of ten with a *Sanitäter*, who would pull our pants down and then lift them up again when we were finished — there was no wiping as there was nothing to wipe with. Many of us had diarrhea from the lousy diet, which made the whole process even more frequent and humiliating.

The Red Cross parcels also stopped coming. When Beesley protested to the Germans, he was told that the parcels were cut off "until the British government apologizes." So it was back to surviving on watery soup and black bread. One day the skeleton of a large rat was found in our soup *Kübel*. Our sergeant called out, "Meat in the soup today, boys!" and held the skeleton aloft. We were all too hungry to care.

The goons untied our wrists in the evening and then tied us up again before the morning *Appell*. One night after their hands were untied three Royals cut a hole in the wire behind the latrine and escaped.

"Wish, I'd known!" said Mackie. "Woulda gone with 'em."

"With your bad foot?" I replied. "Are you nuts?"

Mackie was still limping because of the bullet that had gone through his foot. But he was determined to get better and would walk around the compound at least twice a day, doing twists and knee bends and stretches as best he could with his hands tied. The three Royals who had escaped were captured ten days later. They were made to stand outside against a barracks wall with their hands chained behind them for a full day. If they moved they were jabbed with a rifle butt. Then they were hauled off to "the cooler," a nine-by-sixteen-foot cell, for ten days' solitary confinement.

"Well, at least they didn't shoot 'em," said Mackie, who seemed as determined as ever to make his own escape.

After a few weeks of tying our hands in front of us, the Germans decided they would tie them behind us, instead. Small things we had learned to do with our hands tied in front of us now became impossible. Morale plummeted to an all-time low. We weren't allowed to lie on our bunks during the day, so I often sat on the cement floor with my back against the wall, feeling utterly hopeless. The weather had turned cool and it was hard to stay warm.

One morning I saw Mackie standing over me. "Okay, Allie, up and at 'em," he said. Then he pulled me up and dragged me outside. "I'm worried about you," he went on. "That droopy look of yours reminds me of your dad."

I knew he was referring to the time when my father was unemployed and had just sat smoking and reading the newspapers on our front porch.

"I *am* feeling pretty low," I said, turning to Mackie. "I'd be okay if I just had a book to read. Then I'd have something to look forward to when I woke up in the morning."

"You've read lots of books," replied Mackie. He paused and looked at me and then said, "so why don't you tell me about some of them. You *know* a lot of stuff!"

"So what *stuff* do you want to know?" I asked with a sigh.

"We-e-ll," replied Mackie, "How about Mary Queen of Scots. You remember we saw her palace in Edinburgh?"

"Holyrood House," I said. "Yes, I remember."

"Okay, well, how come they chopped her head off?"

"Whew, that's a long story," I replied. "But," I added with a wry smile, "I guess we have the time."

During our walk, I told him what I knew about Mary Queen of Scots. And that led me the next day to tell him about her cousin, Queen Elizabeth I, whose grave we'd seen in Westminster Abbey. The day after that I told him about Mary's son, King James VI of Scotland, and how he became James I of England after the death of Queen Elizabeth.

"So what about Bonnie Prince Charlie?" Mackie asked. "My dad taught us a song about him."

"I'll get to him. He comes later. But first I have to explain about the Stuart kings," I replied.

By the time I got to the story of Bonnie Charlie, the "prince in the heather," we were into our third week of daily walks and my mood had improved greatly. Thinking about what I was going to tell Mackie each day *did* give me something to look forward to when I opened my eyes in the morning.

"Allie, you really know a *lot* of stuff!" Mackie would say. "When we get out of here you gotta go to college. You could be a teacher, or a professor, or something like that."

Mackie's praise and our daily walks pulled me out of my funk. It helped me forget about the ropes and the barbed wire and my growling, hungry stomach. My wrists were also raw and irritated from the creosote in the ropes. Some of the men had developed nasty sores and purple fingers from it.

During *Appell* on the morning of December 2nd, the camp commandant showed up again. This time we were told that instead of apologizing, Winston Churchill had ordered that German POWs in England should have *their* hands tied. We let out a small cheer. Then we were told that because of Churchill's "obstinacy" our punishment would continue. We booed. Once again we were marched into a barracks, but this time there were shackles waiting for us — handcuffs joined by a chain just over a foot long. Compared to the ropes, however, the shackles seemed a big improvement. You could put your hands in your pockets while wearing them, for instance. With the weather becoming colder and with no gloves to wear, this made a big difference. Best of all, we soon discovered a way to get out of the shackles.

Wilf, of course, was the first man in our hut to figure out how to do it. We'd kept all of the empty cans from the Red Cross parcels and some of them had little tin keys as openers. Wilf managed to shape one of these so that it could unlock the shackles. Soon the guys in all the other huts did likewise. During the day, when Spitfire and his goons weren't looking, we would unlock the shackles. But the punishment for being caught without shackles was severe — eight hours standing against a wall in the cold with hands tied behind the back.

One day, a guard caught a naked soldier from our hut washing himself at the trough in the washroom. He had his shackles on but it was obvious that he must have removed them to take his clothes off. The guard screamed at the naked man and then ran to fetch Spitfire. Some of us rushed in and helped the soldier take off his shackles, get dressed, and then put the chains back on. When the guard returned with Spitfire, the soldier was calmly washing his face fully clothed. Spitfire began screaming at the guard and accused him of being drunk while on duty. This gave us all a big laugh, but taught us to keep a sharp eye for Spitfire and his goons. Whenever one of them was seen approaching our hut, we would call out, "Air Raid!" and quickly put on our shackles.

Keeping clean was not easy because we never knew when the water would be turned on. One day when there was no water at all we saw Beesley striding across the parade ground with soap and towel in hand. He stopped beside a large puddle of freezing water and stripped to the waist. He then proceeded to wash himself and then shave using the water from the frigid puddle. Shortly after this, the water was turned on. Beesley more than lived up to his own advice to "make the enemy fear you." When Spitfire would keep us shivering on the parade ground during winter *Appell*s, Beesley would tear into him. "Hurry up, you idiot!" he would bark out. "Get these lads counted and off parade quickly." Anyone else would have been thrown into the cooler for talking to Spifire that way, but not Beesley. We were all in awe of him.

In the second week of December we had our first snowfall and I awoke to a feathery pile of snow next to my bed, thanks to a broken window. The brick stove in the middle of our hut provided very little heat, particularly with the small ration of coal we were allowed each day. For warming up food, Wilf came up with an ingenious invention. Using Red Cross cans, he created a miniature blower with a tiny hand-cranked fan. It created a current of air that ran through a pipe made of cans to a tin bowl, in which we burned twigs or scraps of cardboard. When a can of water was placed over the bowl it could be brought to a boil quite quickly with air blowing on the fire. Soon most muckers' groups had built their own blowers, though Spitfire delighted in kicking them over whenever he saw them.

The cold concrete floor soon gave me (and others) a bad case of chilblains, a nasty condition that caused your feet to swell up and turn red and itchy. Mackie managed to trade cigarettes with some Brits for a pair of wooden clogs for me. They helped with the chilblains and many of the men began carving their own clogs. We soon became used to the sound of wooden shoes clomping around our hut. Bill managed to find sheets of brown burlap to cover the leaky windows. A couple of the French-speaking FMRs decided to decorate these with murals representing each Canadian province — from leaping salmon for B.C. to a girl with a basket of potatoes for P.E.I.

For Christmas that year, one hut had a large mural depicting the Parliament Buildings in Ottawa with the clock tower shining through a snowfall. A Mohawk soldier from the Essex Scottish drew it with soap on a blanket and it made us all long for home. British Red Cross parcels arrived just before Christmas too — something that raised our spirits considerably. The goons allowed us to keep the chains off from Christmas Eve till the end of Boxing Day and we were spared the *Appell* in the freezing cold on Christmas morning. With the silver paper from cigarette packages we made tinsel and hung it around the brick chimney of our stove. On Christmas Day we sang carols and tried to banish our homesickness. I remember heating water for cocoa for our muckers' group using the handy blower. As we sipped the hot cocoa and ate some tinned plum pudding from the Red Cross parcel, we wished each other a Merry Christmas.

"And may this be the last Christmas we spend in Stalag VIIIB!" said Big Jim.

"Hear, hear!" we replied, the words echoing around our hut.

160

CHAPTER 14
TUNNELLING
February 14, 1943

Kriegsgefangenenpost
14/2/43

Dear Mum:

Many thanks for your letter and parcel, which just arrived. I see that you sent it on November 12, so it took a while to get here. So sorry to hear that you didn't learn that I was still alive until the end of October! I can only imagine how anxious you must have been. Especially after Mrs. McAllister was told that Mackie had been killed at Dieppe. Luckily, he was only wounded and he now sleeps in the bunk above mine. His foot has pretty much healed up and he is walking around quite well.

POW camp is not fun but we are surviving it in good health. And the war can't last forever. Many thanks for the scarf and gloves you knitted. And the books are a godsend! There's a lineup of guys wanting to read the two Agatha Christie mysteries. And I'm savouring every page of Hemingway's

For Whom the Bell Tolls. *Please thank Mrs. Newman at the library for suggesting it.*

I'm not sure how soon I'll be able to receive another package but could you please send some cigarettes? Don't think I've taken up smoking! They're what we use here for money and can be swapped for soap and other necessities.

And please don't worry about me, I'm doing fine. Much love to Elspeth and Doreen.

Your loving son,

Alistair

* * *

Books! I couldn't believe how much I'd missed them. I wasn't a big mystery fan but I devoured Agatha Christie's *Murder on the Orient Express* and *Death on the Nile* in about a day each. I passed them on to Mackie, who was soon renting them out for one cigarette per read. (He said this would prevent pages being torn out for latrine paper.) The parcel from home had arrived right in the middle of the coldest month of a miserable winter when I needed it most. Ernest Hemingway's big fat novel about the Spanish Civil War kept me going right through to the end of March.

By then Mackie had become totally consumed by

the digging of the escape tunnel. All tunnelling had stopped on October 8, the day our hands were tied. The concrete slab had been sealed and the seam disguised with a paste made of milk powder, cocoa and sand. When the ropes were replaced with shackles that we could unlock, tunnelling once again became possible. As the ground began to thaw in March, Beesley decided that work on the tunnel should resume. Mackie soon became one of the keenest tunnellers, volunteering to work late into the night. When the shaft reached three yards in depth, Bill decided they should dig straight out for 40 yards or so, aiming to come up in some bushes beyond the wire. But the soft, sandy soil meant that the tunnel could easily collapse. Soon, most of our bed boards were down in the tunnel, acting as supports for the ceiling and walls. To hold up our mattresses we made nets with the string from the Red Cross parcels and slung them under the sagging palliasses.

As the tunnel lengthened, there was more and more sandy earth to be disposed of without alerting suspicion. During a cold snap in early April, one of the guys decided to spread sand on the icy roadway between our compound and the air force camp next to us. When the goons asked him what he was doing he said he was helping to prevent their trucks from skidding on the ice. And they believed him! A few days later we even received a commendation from the camp commandant for helping to keep the paths and roads safe!

Tin lamps for the tunnel were made with cloth wicks soaked in melted margarine. But black fumes from them sent the diggers up choking and coughing. A French-Canadian named Robichaud created a bellows from a groundsheet that could pump fresh air down into the tunnel through a pipe made of Klim cans. When Mackie worked the night shift as a digger I would often lie on the floor pumping air down to him. He lay on his belly in the tunnel on a trolley made of wooden slats with tin-can wheels. It was often so hot down in the shaft that Mackie and the other diggers would usually work naked. This was easier since any dirt on clothes would have been a giveaway. I would often brush Mackie off when his shift was done and then sweep the ochre soil into a Red Cross box.

"Tunnel's gotta be outside the fence by now," he whispered to me late one night in May, while I was cleaning him up.

"Sure hope so," I replied. "Don't want to pop out right under a goon tower."

Once Bill Lee and Sid Cleasby were fairly sure the tunnel was the right length, they then began to carefully dig upwards. Extra boards were found to build a trap door for the end of the tunnel. Mackie volunteered to help Bill install it — a very risky job since the goons patrolled the compound at night with Alsatian dogs. Bill and Mackie waited for the first moonless night. After midnight they went down into the tunnel in dark clothes with their faces blackened. Mackie went first, carrying a homemade ladder and shovel. Bill followed with the trap door, which was hinged in the middle for easier transport.

I stood near a window holding some matches. If I saw a guard approaching, I was to strike a match in the window as a warning to Mackie.

Mackie's job was to dig out the last few yards of earth from the shaft, place the ladder, and then crawl outside. From there he was to help Bill install the trap door and then cover it with dirt and dead leaves. When all was ready, Bill would open it just enough to allow Mackie to slither back into the tunnel.

As I stood in the shadows by the window, I listened to the sounds of men snoring in their bunks. About fifteen minutes passed. Surely Bill and Mackie should be done by now, I thought.

Spotlights from the goon towers made regular sweeps over the compound. During one of these, I suddenly caught a glimpse of a guard with a dog.

He was walking along the wire right towards the trap door! With shaking hands I found a match. I struck it but it wouldn't light! I took another and struck again. This one sparked into flame and I held it up in the window.

The dog barked and the guard yelled. I fled from the window and dived into my bunk. Then I heard footsteps outside. The barracks door crashed open and the guard shone his flashlight around our bunks. We all lay very still. Spotlights from the goon towers splashed light through the windows. I knew that the trap door was only about 18 yards away from a guard tower.

I lay there frozen, my heart racing. "Please don't shoot Mackie . . . Please don't shoot him . . . Don't shoot, don't shoot . . . No shooting, please, please," I breathed silently in time to my beating heart. Eventually the sound of tramping boots outside died down and my breathing began to slow as well. I lifted my head and peered out the window. All was darkness.

I waited for what seemed a very long time. Then there was a *tap, tap, tap* sound from underneath the concrete slab. In seconds Sid was on top of it and yanking it up with his powerful arms. I soon spied Mackie's white teeth gleaming through his blackened face. He and Bill quickly cleaned themselves up and crawled into their bunks before Spitfire or one of his goons could make another spot check. All too soon, however, Spitfire's snarling tones through the loudspeakers summoned us to yet another morning *Appell*.

It wasn't until Mackie and I took our afternoon walk around the compound that I found out exactly what had happened to him during the night. He said that it had not been easy to fit the trap door inside the hole in pitch darkness. He had been lying on his stomach, reaching down into the shaft, when he spied the lit match in the window. He immediately rolled backwards to get out of spotlight range. When the guard yelled and moved towards the barracks, Mackie dived back even farther into the trees. He said he lay there for a good twenty minutes or so, watching the spotlights sweep by. When they finally stopped, he looked up and caught sight of the barracks inside the barbed wire. He said that he then had to force himself to go back towards the trap door.

"I could *smell* freedom," he told me with his eyes dancing. "It was a spring night in the woods. I wanted to just *take off* like a jackrabbit."

"Sure, and they'd *shoot* you like a jackrabbit, too!" I responded.

"Naw-w-w," he replied, "they'd have to catch me first! But I'll tell you one thing, Allie. There's no way they're gonna keep me chained up in here for years. Just no way."

* * *

Harry Beesley and the escape committee made it clear that they would decide who would be allowed to leave through the tunnel. Beesley said that mass escapes from other camps had ended in disaster. "So we are going to do it differently," he told us, "and make sure that every man who leaves here stands a good chance of getting back to England. Only two men at a time will be allowed to escape. And we will cover for them at roll call for as long as we can. Those of most importance to the war effort will go first."

A few days later, we had a new bunk-mate in 19B. He was an English soldier who had been sentenced to death for committing sabotage on a work party — some English POWs had done work at a nearby brick factory. The condemned man had been smuggled out of his cell and given a Canadian uniform and shackles. Soon he was joined by a newly captured British colonel who was being transferred to another camp, since officers weren't kept at Stalag VIIIB, only sergeants, corporals and ordinary privates like us. The sergeant-major in charge of the British compound had received word from the War Office in London — the Brits got messages through a crystal radio set hidden in their barracks — that this colonel had to escape as quickly as possible.

When new prisoners arrived, the goons usually allowed other POWs to bring food to them. During our welcoming party in the British compound, the colonel switched clothes with a Canadian who looked a little like him. He then returned with us to 19B right under the noses of the guards. The next day the colonel was outfitted in a navy blue suit with a raincoat and a fedora hat. He carried a leather briefcase that had all his faked passes and identification papers, and even a pipe and a tobacco pouch. The soldier who was escaping execution wore a woollen jacket, a peaked cap and wire-rimmed glasses that made him look like a million other workers in Germany. I was astonished at how the British POWs had managed to pull all this together. The navy suit had been tailored from a khaki uniform that had been dyed with beet pulp. The spectacles were made with wire and broken window glass. The briefcase had been acquired by bribing a guard.

But creating the false identity papers was the most amazing feat of all. British POWs who knew German would pore through newspapers filched from the goons. They would find job ads and then carefully forge letters from a company official inviting the recipient for an interview. The cleverest English forgers could even imitate typewriter type using very fine brushes. Everyone in Germany had to carry an identity card and a police pass as well as travel documents. These were duplicated on a hand-turned copying device made with a broom handle and the rubber grip from a cricket bat. They were then stamped with the official-looking insignias each document required. The stamps had been carved out of a potato or the heel of a boot.

It was decided that the colonel and the condemned soldier would escape in broad daylight. The plan was for them to catch a train at the Lamsdorf station that would take them to the city of Dresden. From there they would take other trains until they reached a little town near the Swiss border. A climb through the Alps could then take them safely inside Switzerland, a neutral country in the war.

Early that afternoon, Mackie and I both served as lookouts at the barracks windows. Bill Lee and the two escapees wrapped themselves in burlap palliasse covers to keep their clothes clean. Sid then hoisted the concrete slab and Bill led the two men through the tunnel. Outside in the compound, a game of touch football had been started to distract the guards in the towers. Right at the time the two escaping men were due to crawl out the trap door, one football player socked another on the side of the jaw. As the two of them fell down and wrestled in the dirt, the other players gathered round yelling. The guards in the tower grinned and stood up to get a better look. While they looked the other way, our two "civilians" dashed into the cover of the forest.

Over the next six months, thirty-six men escaped through the tunnel, two at a time. At *Appell* we would cover for the missing men by saying they were sick and in their bunks. When the goons charged in to check, they would always find a sick-looking man in the bunk of the escapee. Another trick was for a couple of us to dodge back in the line after Spitfire had counted us.

Eventually the Germans would discover that there had been an escape. We were then made to stand outside for hours while all of the barracks were torn apart. The goons would bring in poles and tap on the concrete floors, hoping to hear the hollow sound of a tunnel. But after every escape we would fill in the shaft under the hut with loose dirt that was stored in Red Cross boxes hidden under bunks. So the tunnel entrance in 19B was never discovered.

After a while we heard that about half of the men who escaped managed to make it back to England — a very good average, and proof that the escape committee's methods were working. All of the men selected for escape had to be able to speak German or French fluently. This gave the French-Canadian FMRs a real advantage, and many of them were sent through the tunnel disguised as French workers.

* * *

By September, Mackie was getting desperate to escape. He felt he'd earned it.

"Nobody worked harder on that tunnel than me. *Nobody!*" he'd say to me angrily on our afternoon walks.

"I know that, Mack," I'd reply. "But you don't speak any German or French."

"Yeah, but *you* do," he'd say. "We go together and you say I'm deaf or something if we get stopped."

My French was improving from the card games with the FMRs, and I'd picked up some German, too. But I wasn't fluent in either language and I told Mackie his plan just wouldn't work.

As the first anniversary of our year in chains approached in early October of 1943, Mackie was getting desperate. He kept asking Beesley to be put on the escape list, but Beesley was not very encouraging. Mackie was so persistent that Beesley finally arranged a meeting with the English sergeants in charge of the escape committee. When we told them our plan, one suddenly fired a question at me in German about who I was and where I was from. I answered in rather stumbling German that my name was Fritz Schulz and I was from Hamburg. Then the other sergeant asked me in French how I liked the food in Germany. I replied a little more confidently to this question, but I could see that the Englishmen were not impressed. Mackie then described how much work he had done on the tunnel, but that didn't impress them either.

"I'd give you chaps three days at best," one of them finally said. "Within three days you'd be in the hands of the Gestapo and very likely shot."

As we walked back to our hut, Mackie poured out his disappointment to Beesley.

"I tell you what, lad," Beesley replied when Mackie had finished. "Your best bet is to get on a work party and make your escape from there. I can get you a compass so you'll know what direction you're going. If you can get to France, maybe some pretty farmer's daughter will hide you in the barn."

"He-e-ey, that sounds good to me!" said Mackie, cracking a huge smile.

This raised his spirits enormously. But as the days and then weeks passed, no work party passes came his way. More of the Brits had been deliberately damaging equipment at the brick factory, so the owners weren't so willing to take POWs as workers.

I was beginning to worry about Mackie. I'd hear him thrashing about in the bunk overhead during the night. Each morning when they would fasten the shackles around his wrists, he would get red in the face. I began to fear he might slug one of the goons. The Germans would often play Lord Haw Haw's broadcasts over the loudspeakers, describing all the glorious German victories that had happened recently. Mackie would listen with a stony face.

"Don't listen to that baloney!" I'd tell him. "I've heard that the Russians are pushing out the Jerries. And our guys and the Yanks have landed in Italy! We're gonna win this thing!"

"Yeah, well big bloody help *we* are," he shot back. "Stuck in here in chains!"

One day the Germans plastered big posters all around the camp. *The Escape from Prison Camps Is No Longer a Sport!* ran the headline. *England has opened up a non-military form of gangster war!* was stated below it in bold red letters. The text further down announced that *Escaping prisoners of war will almost certainly lose their lives.*

That same day a rumour tore through the camp that we were being transferred to a work camp deep inside Poland. Escape from there would be very difficult, we knew — especially during winter, which was fast approaching.

Mackie was becoming more agitated by the day. Two FMRs were being readied for an escape. Everyone thought they might be the last men to get away from Stalag VIIIB through the tunnel. Soon the earth was removed from the shaft and stored in boxes. I became very afraid that Mackie was going to make a break for it on his own. When I quizzed him about it he'd just wave me away. I'd tell him how crazy and dangerous it would be to try it, but he'd simply give me an odd smile. He began to avoid me — I think he thought I was spying on him. The night after Bill Lee took the two FMRs through the tunnel, I lay awake, listening for any rustling sounds from the palliasse above me. The earth was still out of the tunnel in boxes.

When I awoke to the sound of the morning loudspeakers I realized I'd dozed off. I jumped up to check Mackie's bunk. Empty! I ran through the washroom and then out to the latrine. I couldn't find him anywhere. My heart was pounding crazily. I grabbed Wilf and asked him if he'd seen Mackie. He said he'd heard him get up in the night, but just figured he had to pee.

I asked Wilf to cover for me at *Appell*. I crawled into Mackie's bunk and played sick when the goons came looking. The word soon got out that Mackie had escaped. Bill made sure the earth was put back in the tunnel in a hurry.

By the afternoon, the Germans realized there had been an escape and the barracks were torn apart once again. They never found the entrance from 19B, but they did find the trap door outside the wire. We watched as Russian prisoners poured excrement from the honey pit down into the tunnel. The escape shaft was then sealed with concrete.

In the days that followed, scarcely a minute went by when I didn't think of Mackie. At night I'd have dreams about him sleeping in haystacks or stealing food from barns. "Please don't shoot him," I would silently pray. "Please don't shoot him."

But a week later I had to write a letter that would be etched on my memory forever.

Stalag VIIIB

November 11, 1943

Dear Mrs. McAllister:

By now you have probably heard that Mackie was killed after escaping from our POW camp. I can't begin to tell you how sorry I am that he is dead. I miss him every day and so do all his mates here in the camp. He was the most popular soldier in our hut with his ready smile and big laugh. I keep hearing stories about Mackie's kindnesses to others. And I have so many stories of my own.

At Camp Borden, where I was the worst soldier in our training platoon, Mackie helped me through every part of it. I wouldn't have made it without him.

At Dieppe he was a very brave soldier, one of the few who made it off the beach. Here in prison camp, I felt very down in the dumps during our first months here. Mackie wouldn't let me give in, and got me through another very tough period.

He was the bravest, kindest, most remarkable person I've ever known. I will think of him with gratitude every day for as long as I live.

I send my sincerest condolences to you and to all of Mackie's sisters and brothers.

In great sadness and sympathy,

Alistair Morrison

CHAPTER 15

THE LONG MARCH

November 21, 1943

One day in late November the goons took our shackles away. But I barely noticed. I was almost beyond caring what happened to me. After Mackie was killed, I never smiled and rarely spoke to anyone. When I heard that some of us were being transferred to another camp, I simply shrugged. Nothing could be worse than Stalag VIIIB. And every miserable inch of Hut 19B reminded me of Mackie. At night I had endless dreams where I was trying to save him from being shot. And every morning I woke up to his empty bunk above mine.

On November 26, Harry Beesley led about three hundred of us to the Lamsdorf train station, where once again we were crammed into filthy boxcars. Our destination was another POW camp, Stalag IID, outside a town called Stargard near Stettin, a port on the Baltic Sea. After a day's travel we entered Stalag IID's gloomy gates. Harry Beesley lined us up and the camp commandant came to inspect us.

"*Sie sollen hier arbeiten,*" was his curt greeting. I knew enough German by then to make out that he was saying, "You are here to work!" He then harangued us about the dangers of escapes and concluded with the Heil Hitler salute. Boos and catcalls followed, though not from me.

Despite this chilly welcome, we soon found that the conditions at Stalag IID were generally better than at VIIIB. The guards were soldiers who had served in battle and they were much less harsh than Spitfire and his goons. The food was just as bad, but most of the POWs went out on work parties and brought back food that they had bartered for cigarettes. Before leaving VIIIB I had received a package from my mother with several cartons of cigarettes, so I was able to swap them for some extra food. But even a full stomach didn't stop me from feeling like a dead man walking.

Harry Beesley noticed how withdrawn I'd become since Mackie's death and suggested that I talk to Padre Foote. John Foote was the chaplain for the Hamilton Rileys. He had volunteered to come to Stargard from an officers' POW camp. I'd heard a lot about him — how he had picked up wounded men under fire on the beach at Dieppe and carried them out to the boats. I'd been told that Foote was pulled into one of the boats as it was leaving, but he had jumped back into the water, saying, "My place is with the boys." I remembered him walking with us on the way to Envermeu.

I didn't feel like talking much to anybody, but I eventually agreed to see Padre Foote. I told him about my friendship with Mackie and how he had died. The padre told me that it was understandable that I felt guilty about Mackie's death. "Those of us who survive always wonder, Why us and not them?" he said. "And we sometimes think that we should have died instead of them." He told me that he still saw the bodies on the beach at Dieppe in his dreams almost every night.

I soon found that talking with him actually helped. I particularly liked the fact that he never tried to push God or religion on me. After a few meetings with him, I began to sleep better at night and to talk to others a little more often.

Near Stargard were large state-run farms where we were soon sent to work. In February 1944, after another group of Canadians from VIIIB arrived, we were sent away from the camp for weeks or even months at a time, usually in groups of twenty. On the farms, we would sleep in barns or sheds. The guards were generally quite old, as all the younger men were required at the Front. I remember one guard who had been a cavalry officer in the First

World War, a kindly old gent who liked to read and would occasionally lend me some books in German. I would try to struggle through them in my off hours using a German–English dictionary provided to German soldiers.

There was little machinery on these farms and no gasoline to run it, since that was reserved for army trucks and tanks. Most of the work was done by hand — I remember many days of planting potatoes and later harvesting them, and learning how to guide a plough pulled by two old horses.

On some of the farms, groups of young German women would help out in the fields, though we were kept strictly away from them after work hours. We were told repeatedly that any POW caught fraternizing with a German woman would be shot. Many of the guys flirted with them anyway. One hot summer day some of us decided to take a swim in a farm pond. We drew a crowd of ogling young women and had to cover ourselves as quickly as we could!

Life on the farms was monotonous but bearable. After a day's hard labour I would generally fall into a deep, dreamless sleep. But never again did I feel the sheer joy of being alive. That seemed to have departed with Mackie's death. And hunger constantly gnawed at me, since our rations were the familiar watery soup and black bread. From time to time, Red Cross parcels would find their way to us, and we would be able to get a few sausages or vegetables from some of the farm workers in exchange for soap or chocolate bars. For German civilians these luxury items were in short supply. As 1943 turned into 1944, they became even scarcer. By then we knew from the scraps of news we heard that the war was going badly for Germany. After the Allies landed in Normandy on D-Day — June 6, 1944 — word of the invasion quickly spread. Even the Germans knew about it, though one of the guards insisted, "They will be driven back into the sea. Just as you were."

Before long, Allied planes flying overhead on bombing missions became a common sight. We also heard that the Russians were steadily advancing from the east towards the German border. After D-Day the Red Cross parcels began arriving more often. We also noticed that the nastier guards became a little more correct in their attitude towards us. We figured they were worried about how they would be treated if Germany lost the war.

By late January of 1945 we were back inside Stalag IID. We could hear the sound of big guns booming in the distance and knew that the Russians were advancing towards Stargard. On the morning of

February 2, the camp's loudspeakers crackled. We were told to return to our huts to await special orders. There was an excited buzz as rumours flew. Were we going to be handed over to the Russians?

Our mood was quickly dampened when the commandant announced that we were being marched out of the camp. The weather was blisteringly cold, with high winds and heavy snow. We were allowed to take only one blanket. Some of us used it to tie up our extra clothes and any food remaining from our Red Cross parcels. I saw one man packing up the shackles he'd saved from VIIIB as a souvenir. Others tore apart the bunks to made sleds to transport their belongings.

We were marched out of the camp into the howling wind. Men dragged their sleds over snowdrifts. Soon articles of clothing and other belongings were abandoned by the roadside. I saw Padre Foote limping along using a stick to support his one bad leg. I offered to help carry his knapsack but he waved me off. By nightfall we had reached the outskirts of the port of Stettin, where we were joined by thousands of German refugees fleeing the advancing Russians. Some of them were hoping to board boats leaving Stettin. Others were just trudging grimly westward pushing baby carriages, or dragging sleds piled with family belongings. I saw a teenage girl carrying a canary in a cage and a boy cradling a puppy. There were a few farm carts with some carrots or potatoes stowed in them, so bartering began in earnest. I swapped a chocolate bar for a handful of carrots. That night as we bedded down in a chilly barn, I shared the carrots with a muckers' group I'd joined. They made a welcome addition to the watery soup.

Early the next morning to cries of *"Raus! Raus!"* from the guards we once again began our weary slog through the snow. I was grateful for the woollen balaclava my mother had sent me. I also had an extra pair of socks, so I could change the wet ones each night. Many of the other men suffered from frostbite on their ears and toes.

For twelve days we trudged onwards with frozen eyebrows and beards. At night we slept in farm buildings. Our food rations dwindled and bartering became ever harder, as the German civilians had so little food to spare. On one railway siding we saw a flatbed car piled with turnips. A group of us grabbed as many as we could and ate them raw — and got stomach cramps as a result.

On the thirteenth day we saw a sight that made our hearts race. On the road ahead of us stood four trucks with large Red Cross symbols on their sides. How had they found us? I wondered. The sergeants took charge of distributing the food parcels. There was only one for every eight men, but even that seemed like manna from heaven. The parcels had soap in them, which was of little use to us since washing was nearly impossible. Besides, the itching from fleas and body lice seemed the least of our problems. I remember one of my fellow muckers, Ron Reynolds, calling out *"Seife! Seife!"* and showing his bar of soap to people we would pass, and eventually getting a little food in exchange for it.

Ron's foraging prowess was amazing. One day we entered an old medieval town where we saw rows of rabbit hutches filled with plump rabbits. As we passed by, Ron quickly opened the hutch of the largest rabbit and stuffed it under his jacket.

That night visions of rabbit stew danced in our heads as we sat in the hayloft of a barn. But none of us had the heart to kill it. Finally a farm boy from Saskatchewan did the deed for us and the rabbit went into our cooking tin. As the odour of rabbit stew wafted upwards a group of guards entered the barn looking for the missing animal. One of them shone his flashlight into our pot but Ron had cleverly put stones on top of the rabbit meat. A full packet of cigarettes was shoved into the goon's palm and he left us to enjoy our rabbit stew.

For the next seven days we trudged onwards until we reached the train station in the town of

Lübeck. There we were loaded into overcrowded boxcars, standing shoulder to shoulder without room for anyone to lie down. For six days and nights we were shunted across Germany, with only a little black bread to eat and very little water. When we eventually stumbled out into the sunshine, many of the men could barely walk. Nonetheless, we were marched on to a camp near a town called Sandbostel.

By now it was the first week of March and we were grateful for the warming sun and the melting snow by the roadside. But the camp at Sandbostel was worse than anything we had seen so far, a place for people the Nazis considered their political enemies. The prisoners had shaved heads and wore striped pajamas. Open sores covered their hands and faces. Huge, mournful eyes stared out at us from hollowed faces as we marched past them. We tossed them what little food we had.

The next morning we awoke to an even more shocking sight. A railway that ran through the camp passed right near our barracks. We watched in stunned silence as open boxcars packed with stiff, emaciated corpses slowly passed by the windows.

"I knew the Nazis were bad," I heard one POW say quietly, "but *this*, this is just *evil!*"

I thought of Mackie and of how outraged he would have been at seeing this.

We knew, however, that we were witnessing the dying days of Hitler's regime. On March 8 we heard that American troops had crossed the Rhine River. But our ordeal was not yet over. After only a few days in Sandbostel we were on the march again. And six weeks later, the Germans still had us on the move. Word was passed to us to hang on, that it would not be long before we were liberated. On April 26, as we walked along a road south of the city of Hamburg, an RAF squadron spotted us from the air. The planes swooped low and waggled their wings. The guards immediately forced us to turn around and march in the opposite direction. When the RAF planes returned they mistook us for German soldiers. Screaming downwards, they machine-gunned right along our column. We dived for the ditches, but eighty-nine men were killed by the strafing. We buried them by the side of the road, feeling utterly crushed. Several men near me were weeping, but I had become so accustomed to death I felt beyond tears. One of the dead men was from our muckers' group, an engineer named Tommy from Winnipeg. It seemed particularly cruel for him to have been killed in this way, after having survived so much.

Three days later, as we trudged along a roadway, two British tanks and a motorcyle came around a corner ahead of us. We raised our arms and bellowed at the top of our lungs that we were Allied soldiers, that we were Canadians. The German guards immediately threw down their rifles and ran away. We crowded around the British tanks, cheering until we were hoarse. The British soldiers were shocked by how emaciated we were. The sickest POWs were put on trucks and then flown back to England. The rest of us were taken to the British headquarters in a town called Lüneberg. There we were deloused and given hot showers — our first in years. That evening we were fed royally, but we were cautioned not to eat too much, as this was dangerous for men in our condition. I looked around the room at the shining faces of men who hadn't smiled in months. But then I remembered how Mackie's face used to light up when he smiled and I was suddenly struck with a desperate sadness.

On the first day of May an English soldier showed me a newspaper with the headline *HITLER DEAD*. The day before, the *Führer* had shot himself in the head in an underground bunker as Russian troops overran Berlin. The English soldier said that he wished the Russkies had captured him and hung him from a lamppost. But I couldn't think of any punishment that would be sufficient for a man who had unleashed so much horror on the world.

* * *

Three days later, a group of us sat on a hillside outside Lüneberg to watch the commander of Nazi forces in northern Germany surrender to British Field Marshal Bernard Montgomery. One or two former POWs noted the irony of Montgomery being there, since he had been one of the planners of the doomed Dieppe raid over two years and eight months before.

The next day I was shipped back to England, to Aldershot, where I was soon put into hospital with pneumonia. By mid-July I had recovered enough to be sent back to Canada. My mother and sisters met me at the train station, along with Elspeth's new husband, a man I'd never met before.

On my first night home I slept upstairs in my old bedroom on Hiawatha Road. I woke to find my mother shaking me.

"What's wrong?" I asked groggily.

"You were screaming, son," she said. "Having a bad dream. But it's over now, you're home."

"Over?" I asked with a croak.

"Yes," she replied. "It's over and you're home."

But she was wrong. It wasn't over for me. It wouldn't ever be over.

EPILOGUE

After Alistair Morrison's death on September 9, 2009, this letter was found with his will. It was in a sealed envelope addressed to his grandson Lachlan. On it was written NOT TO BE OPENED UNTIL AFTER MY DEATH.

August 19, 2007

Dear Lachlan:

If you're reading this letter, then you already know that your old grandpa has "gone West," as we used to say in the Army. I'm writing this letter on the 65th anniversary of the Dieppe Raid. I know that today some of the men I served with will be standing on Blue Beach for a memorial service. When the band plays "O Canada," these old men in their berets and medals will salute and people will cry.

I always remember this day in my own way.

But I've never wanted to go back to that beach. Nor have I ever wanted to join the Legion and swap war stories — stories that get more embellished with every telling. However, there is one war story that I have never told anyone. It has lain in my heart as a terrible secret for sixty-three years. For a long time, I tried to cover over what really happened in Stalag VIIIB and how Mackie really died. I think I needed to do that to survive. But now that I'm an old man, the urge to tell someone the truth about it weighs very heavily on me.

I hope you will forgive me for unloading this burden on you, Lachlan. But you're the only person to whom I think I can entrust this. You're also the only person who has read my account of what happened to me at Dieppe and afterwards. But the story that I told there about how Mackie died is a lie.

You may remember me describing how distraught I was in October of 1943 when Mackie became so determined to escape from Stalag VIIIB. That part is all true. I knew that he was going to make a break through the tunnel he'd worked so hard to build. I also knew that he would almost certainly be captured, and very likely shot. When he refused to talk to me about it, I felt really hurt. The thought of having to survive in that camp without him filled me with gloom.

On the day that I knew he was going to escape, I became desperate. I racked my brains to think of a way to stop him. The two FMRs had escaped the night before and the tunnel entrance would soon be filled with dirt. I knew that Mackie would try to make a break for it that night.

During that afternoon there was a soccer game going on behind the compound — playing soccer in shackles wasn't easy but we managed. I went into our hut and saw that it was empty. I grabbed one of the Red Cross boxes filled with soil. Walking outside with it under my arm, I headed for the guards' barracks. A few of them were outside enjoying an off-duty cigarette. I walked by them, but when I was still where they could see me, I deliberately tripped. As I fell over, the box hit the ground and its contents spilled out. I quickly scooped the sandy soil back into the box, hurried back to the hut and stowed the box back under a bunk. I don't think any of the other POWs saw me, but I was sure the guards had. And I knew that they understood where the sand in the box had come from.

Before long, there were cries of "Raus, Raus!" as Spitfire and the goons conducted one of their "routine searches." They began next door in 19A, tearing apart bunks and throwing clothes and blankets out the door and windows. By the time they got to 19B, a crowd had gathered outside. The goons had brought poles with them and were tapping the concrete floor. All of a sudden I saw Mackie racing red-faced from behind the barracks. He pushed through the crowd and charged into 19B. I heard yelling and swearing from inside and a few minutes later, three guards dragged out a struggling and kicking Mackie and hauled him off to the cooler. I felt guilty about this, but thought that at least he would be safe there. A half hour later, a very proud Spitfire was able to show the camp commandant the "prize" he had so cleverly discovered. The next day the entrance shaft to the tunnel was filled with poured concrete.

They kept Mackie in the cooler for two weeks. Work began almost immediately on another tunnel from Hut 22B. There was also talk of the Germans having planted a spy among us who had given away the location of the first tunnel. Then rumours about us being transferred to another camp began circulating. I tried to get word to Mackie in the cooler. I wanted to tell him that it would be easier to escape from the new camp. But the goons wouldn't allow him any visitors.

I didn't know that Mackie had been let out of the cooler until I heard the noise. Our whole compound was cheering as he was put into line at the evening Appell. He seemed very pale and a little shaky. When I went towards him later he only stared at me very coolly. After they took our shackles off that night he crawled straight into his bunk. I thought he was just overtired and would feel more like talking in the morning.

The sound of a siren outside woke me up. Spotlights were sweeping the compound. I ran to the window and saw a man climbing the fence. I knew immediately that it was Mackie. The guard in the nearest tower fired shots over his head, but Mackie kept on going. He leapt across to the second fence. He must have had a wire cutter, because he managed to cut through the barbed wire at the top of the outside fence. Machine-gun fire ricocheted around him, but I saw him jump to the ground and begin to turn away. It was only then that he was caught in a hail of bullets.

"No!" I wailed as I saw him fall. "Please! No, no, no!"

I yanked on my boots and ran out of the hut. Outside the fence, some guards had picked Mackie up and were carrying him back to the main gate. I ran to the gate of our compound. They were taking him to the infirmary. I prayed that he was only wounded. Suddenly I was grabbed by two goons and swung around to face Spitfire.

"Please! I must see him!" I stammered in my broken German, pointing to the infirmary. "He is my friend!"

"Sein Freund? — *his friend?*" sneered Spitfire, imitating my voice. Then he spat out the words that have haunted me ever since. "Sie sind sein Judas!"

I took a step back, shocked. Spitfire had said, "You are his Judas!"

The guards hauled me back to the hut. The next morning at Appell I heard that Mackie had died in the night. We buried him in the camp cemetery the next day. The word *Judas* — that damning word that Spitfire had hissed at me — echoed constantly in my ears. The thought that I had betrayed my friend, the best man I had ever known, made me want to die. There were many times when I thought of simply heading for the wire myself.

One of the things Padre Foote said to me at Camp IID was that we had to live for those who had died. So I resolved to live for Mackie's sake. After returning home, Lachlan, I decided to go to university and become a history teacher, just as he had said I should. Your father is named Hamish after Mackie — a name he never liked. But still the thought that I had helped bring about Mackie's death would sometimes overwhelm me. It nearly killed me to have to lie to Mackie's family about how he had died.

About six months after I came home I had what in those days was called a nervous breakdown. I was *in hospital for a while and then in a convalescent home for veterans. While I was recovering I met your wonderful grandmother, who was a nurse there. I never told her the whole story of how Mackie died — just about the crippling guilt I felt for having survived. She, too, persuaded me that it was my duty to live my life in honour of Mackie and the others who never came home.*

That is what I have tried to do, Lachlan. And that is why I've written about my war experiences for you. There are so many terrible things about war. But one of the most horrifying is that colossal mistakes are made — mistakes that cost thousands of lives. Mistakes that mark the lives of those who survive, sometimes forever.

I can only hope and pray, Lachlan, that you, and your children and grandchildren, if you have them, will be spared from wars and the horrors they inflict.

I leave you my warmest wishes for a long and happy life.

Your loving grandpa,

Alistair Morrison

In another, larger envelope, Lachlan Morrison found a slightly scorched, leather-bound copy of *Rob Roy* by Sir Walter Scott and a photograph of three young Canadian soldiers in Trafalgar Square with pigeons perched on their arms and shoulders. Also included was a war service medal and a small bronze bar that said *Dieppe*. Both were still in wrappers that had never been opened.

HISTORICAL NOTE

The Dieppe Raid haunts us still. We wonder how it could have happened. How could so many Canadians have been sent to die there?

A good place to begin to answer these questions is on the beaches of another French town called Dunkirk. There, two years before Dieppe, thousands of British and French soldiers were trapped as Hitler's armies overran France. By the end of May 1940, it looked as if tens of thousands of Allied soldiers would either be killed or captured. Then from every port in southern England came ships of all kinds. They sailed across the English Channel and rescued over 338,000 soldiers.

What soon became known as "the miracle of Dunkirk" was a great morale booster for the British. Prime Minister Winston Churchill had to remind his people that a rescue was not a victory. Churchill knew that the British were now in no shape to attack Hitler's Fortress Europe.

Then a top-secret plan landed on Churchill's desk. It proposed the formation of a small force of raiders that would assault and disrupt the enemy. Immediately, some of their toughest soldiers were sent to the highlands of Scotland for fierce training. Only a few weeks after Dunkirk, a raiding party of 120 men crept across the English Channel by night and blew up a German facility. The newspapers cheered. Bigger and more ferocious raids followed.

The Canadian generals noted the success of these raids. Why couldn't our men be part of them, they asked. By the fall of 1941 there were 125,000 Canadian soldiers in England who hadn't seen any action yet. People were beginning to wonder why the Canadians weren't fighting. The man in charge of planning raids was the young, handsome and ambitious Lord Louis Mountbatten. Mountbatten's team had chosen Dieppe as one of several ports in Nazi-occupied France to be targeted for possible small raids in early 1942. But soon plans were afoot to make Dieppe a "super-raid" that would involve five thousand men from the 2nd Canadian Division. They would attack and capture the town and then retreat — showing Hitler that he was vulnerable.

The raid on Dieppe was code-named Operation

Rutter. Each time the British commanders met to review the plan for Rutter, however, it was changed. Before long, all that the plan had going for it was the element of surprise and a belief that Dieppe was not strongly defended. Meanwhile, the men of the 2nd Canadian Division were undergoing intensive training on the Isle of Wight. On the night of July 2, 1942, they boarded ships for what they thought was yet another training exercise. Instead, they were told that tomorrow they would attack Hitler's Fortress Europe in a raid on Dieppe. The men cheered, thrilled that they would finally see some action. But the next day they learned the raid had been postponed. For the next four days, the Canadians waited in the hot, stuffy ships for the order to go. Then, at dawn on July 7, four German planes swooped down and bombed the troopships lying at anchor. Amazingly, there were only a few casualties. The men were taken ashore and later told that the Dieppe raid had been cancelled. They were bitterly disappointed.

Within a week, however, Mountbatten had raised the idea of remounting the raid. At first the generals scoffed. Everyone knew about the aborted raid on Dieppe — surely the enemy would be prepared for an attack?

Mountbatten argued that the Germans would never expect the Allies to attack the same target again. He also stated that if they did not attack Dieppe, there would be no chance for another raid that summer. The generals knew that Soviet leader Josef Stalin was insisting that the British should invade France and force Hitler to divert some of his troops from Russia. He was even threatening to make a separate peace with Hitler if the British did not comply. On July 24, Churchill approved a remounting of the Dieppe Raid, to be named Operation Jubilee.

On the afternoon of August 18, 1942, the men of the 2nd Division were once again loaded onto ships and told they were going to attack Dieppe. This time no-one cheered. The first thing to go wrong happened after the ships had crossed through the enemy minefield off the French coast. Some of the landing boats carrying the commandos towards Yellow Beach ran into a German convoy. A fire-fight erupted, a British gunboat was damaged, and the commandos' landing craft were scattered. Despite this, some of the British commandos, who were responsible for taking out the big gun batteries on either side of Dieppe, did manage to attack some of their targets. But these were among the few successes of the raid.

At Green Beach, just west of Dieppe, the South Saskatchewan Regiment landed without being detected and quickly seized control of the village of Pourville. But despite some brave fighting, the Saskatchewans soon found they could proceed no farther towards Dieppe. The Queen's Own Cameron Highlanders of Winnipeg had landed at Green Beach after the Saskatchewans and they, too, were halted from advancing on Dieppe by enemy gunfire.

At Blue Beach, the enemy saw the Royal Regiment come ashore at dawn and greeted them with gunfire and mortars. Of the 250 men in the first wave, only a handful made it to the seawall. The Royals suffered the worst casualties of any regiment; 225 of them were killed and 264 taken prisoner. The men landing on the main town beaches, which were code-named Red and White, were also met with withering enemy fire. The tanks of the Calgary Tanks Regiment either got stuck on the pebbled beach or were unable to advance any farther than the concrete promenade just beyond the beach. Some men from the Royal Hamilton Light Infantry, however, did manage to seize the town's white casino building, and a few men from Windsor's Essex Scottish regiment made it into the streets of the town. When the raid's commander, General

Ham Roberts, heard of this, it encouraged him to send in his reserve troops, the men of the Fusiliers Mont-Royal of Montreal. But when the FMRs came ashore, they, too, were trapped in blazing gunfire.

It was not until 9:40 a.m. that Ham Roberts, in his command ship offshore, realized that the raid had utterly failed. With an ashen face he issued the coded order to withdraw. But rescuing the men still alive from the body-strewn beaches would be no easy task. After several attempts, Roberts instructed the offshore fleet to sail for England. Remaining behind were 3367 men, 2752 of them Canadians — dead or soon to be taken prisoner. Of the 1027 men who died, 907 were Canadians. As one survivor remembers, "Anyone who was on that beach will tell you that the water was just like red ink with blood and body parts washing ashore." It is for this reason that the Dieppe Raid has been called "the bloodiest nine hours in Canadian military history."

Despite the raid's failure, it has been claimed that "valuable lessons" were learned at Dieppe which helped lead to success on D-Day in June of 1944, and to the eventual defeat of Nazi Germany. Certainly the Allies would never again try to attack an enemy port. But today most historians agree that the price of learning at Dieppe was far too high.

On the morning of September 1, 1944, the men of the 2nd Canadian Division marched into a liberated Dieppe to be greeted with flowers and champagne. That afternoon they went to a graveyard with small wooden crosses to pay tribute to the more than one thousand men who had died there two years before. On every August 19 since then, the town of Dieppe has been draped in Canadian flags. In the square, called Square du Canada, crowds gather around a monument that bears the inscription: *On the beaches of Dieppe, our Canadian cousins marked with their blood the road to our final liberation.*

Canadian soldiers board a transport ship in preparation for the Dieppe Raid in the summer of 1942.

Soldiers charge ashore from a beach landing craft with weapons in hand.

By 9:00 a.m. on August 19, 1942, there were 225 men lying dead by the seawall on Blue Beach.

Captured Canadians are marched through the streets of Dieppe.

The men of Hut 19B in Stalag VIIIB (top) pose for
a photo. With homemade shovels (below), the Canadians
dig escape tunnels from the camp.

After a four-month death march during the bitter winter of 1945, the soldiers who survived were severely emaciated.

*Some of the men who survived the Dieppe Raid
and prison camp were (upper) Private Ron Reynolds
of Toronto's Royal Regiment of Canada, (lower left)
Sergeant-Major Harry Beesley of the British Number Three
Commando Group and (lower right) Padre John Foote.*

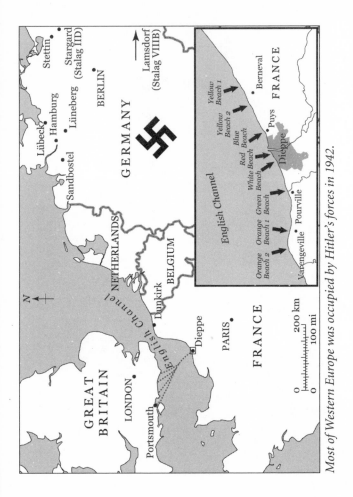

Most of Western Europe was occupied by Hitler's forces in 1942.

GLOSSARY

Allies: the nations — including Great Britain, the United States, the Soviet Union, Canada and others — that fought against Germany, Japan and Italy during World War II.

army units: The **Canadian army** during World War II had 5 **divisions.** The **2nd Division,** which fought at Dieppe, was made up of 3 **brigades**; each **brigade** had 3 **regiments,** also called **battalions.** A **battalion** had 5 **companies** made up of 3 **platoons** of approximately 35 soldiers each. Along with a headquarters company and a support company, a battalion usually numbered 600–800 men.

artillery: weapons such as big guns and cannons.

bandolier: a broad belt worn over the shoulder by soldiers, with small loops or pockets for holding bullets.

battery: a defensive position from which guns are fired.

Blitz: from *Blitzkrieg,* a German word meaning "lightning war" that refers to the bombing of Britain by Nazi Germany between September 7, 1940 and May 10, 1941.

Bren gun: A lightweight machine gun with a bipod that held up the barrel when the gun was fired from a fixed position. A **Bren gun carrier** was a small armoured vehicle that ran on treads like a tank.

buttress: a prop or support built to steady a structure.

chevron: a V-shaped stripe embroidered on an army uniform. One chevron signified a **lance-corporal**, two a **corporal** and three a **sergeant**. Soldiers of these ranks were called NCOs (non-commissioned officers) and were not considered to be ranking officers.

commando: member of a special fighting force used to make destructive raids; the name was first used in the Boer War.

convoy: a group of ships travelling together with a protective escort.

destroyer: a small, fast, warship usually armed with guns and torpedoes.

Luftwaffe: the German air force during World War II.

militia: a volunteer military force that is called on in times of emergency.

minesweeper: a ship that clears away floating and underwater explosive mines.

mortar: a portable weapon used to fire shells at high angles over short distances.

Nazi: a member of the political party, headed by Adolf Hitler, that held power in Germany from 1933–1945.

Padre: a name that means "father," used for a chaplain in military service.

palliasse: mattresse filled with straw.

pillbox: a low-roofed concrete gun emplacement for a machine gun or anti-tank gun.

POW: a prisoner of war.

private: the lowest ranking soldier in the army.

RAF: Royal Air Force.

Rileys: a nickname for the soldiers of the Royal Hamilton Light Infantry.

"Scots wha hae": words that begin the Scottish national anthem: "Scots wha hae wi' Wallace bled." (Scots who have with Wallace bled.) William Wallace is the Scottish hero depicted in the movie *Braveheart.*

seawall: a wall built to protect a beach from being washed away.

shells/shellfire: explosive rounds fired by **artillery.**

Sten gun: a British submachine gun used throughout World War II, known for its simple design and low production cost.

tube ladder: a lightweight ladder made of aluminum tubing that was carried in five-foot lengths.

U-boat: from the German word "*Unterseeboot,*" meaning submarine.

ACKNOWLEDGMENTS

Grateful acknowledgment is made for permission to reprint the following:

Cover cameo: *Private Lefebvre, Royal Canadian Army Service (R.C.A.S.C.) who is wearing a version of the Canadian Parachute Qualifying Badge, Ottawa, Ontario, Canada, 19 March, 1943*, Lieut. Ken Bell / Canada. Dept. of National Defence, Library and Archives Canada / PA-198346.

Cover scene: *Canadian infantrymen taking part in an assault landing training exercise, Seaford, England, 8 May, 1942*, Library and Archives Canada / PA-144598.

Cover details: (front cover) Aged journal © Shutterstock/Bruce Amos; aged paper © Shutterstock/Filipchuck Oleg Vasilovich; Tape © Phase4Photography; belly band © ranplett/istockphoto; (back cover) label © Shutterstock/Thomas Bethge.

Page 205: *Canadian troops embarking in landing craft during training exercise before raid on Dieppe, France, ca. August 1942*, Canada. Dept. of National Defence/Library and Archives Canada, PA-113244.
Page 206: *Commandos charge ashore from a landing craft during training in Scotland, 28 February 1942*; Lockeyear W (Lt), Malindine E G (Lt)/Imperial War Museum, H 17477.
Page 207: courtesy of Terence Macartney-Filgate Collection.
Page 208: courtesy of Jayne Poolton-Turvey.
Page 209 (upper): Hut 19B, Stalag VIIIB, courtesy of Fred Engelbrecht.
Page 209 (lower): courtesy of Terence Macartney-Filgate Collection.
Page 210: *Emaciated former-POWs at Stalag 11B at Fallingbostel, 17 April, 1945*, Hardy (Sgt)/Imperial War Museum, BU 3865.
Page 211 (upper): Private Ron Reynolds of Toronto's Royal Regiment of Canada, courtesy of Ron Reynolds.
Page 211 (lower left): Sergeant-Major Harry Beesley of the British Number Three Commando Group, courtesy of Jack Beesley.

Page 211 (lower right): Padre John Foote, courtesy of Royal Hamilton Light Infantry Museum.
Page 212: Map by Paul Heersink/Paperglyphs.

The publisher wishes to thank Dr. J. L. Granatstein, author of *The Generals: The Canadian Army's Senior Commanders in the Second World War*; *In Canada's Army: Waging War and Keeping the Peace*; and *Who Killed Canadian History?*, for sharing his historical expertise; and Barbara Hehner for her careful checking of the factual details.

AUTHOR'S NOTE

Although *Prisoner of Dieppe* is a novel, the events described in it all actually took place. Alistair and Mackie are fictional characters, but their experiences are similar to those of real-life soldiers. Sergeant-Major Kewley, Sergeant Hartley and Lieutenant Whitman are also fictional, as is Private Pullio. But all the other characters — from commanders Hedley Basher and Douglas Catto to Stalag VIIIB's Spitfire to Harry Beesley, Sid Cleasby and Bill Lee — are real people.

So is Chaplain John Foote, who became the first Canadian chaplain to be awarded the Victoria Cross, the highest award for gallantry in the British Commonwealth. He died in 1988; the armouries on James Street in Hamilton, Ontario, are named for him. Stan Darch, who received a pair of shoes on the march into captivity, still lives in Hamilton and attends the Hamilton Dieppe commemoration each year on August 19.

The family of Ron Reynolds had a special commemoration on August 19, 2010, when they scattered Ron's ashes on Blue Beach at Dieppe, as he had requested in his will.

Ron Reynolds always spoke of Harry Beesley with awe. The man who helped so many others in Stalag VIIIB never came home after the war. In December of 1944 Beesley escaped from prison camp into Poland and before long was on a rickety old train headed south to a port where he hoped to catch a boat to England. While the train was stopped at a station, the two rear train cars became uncoupled and began to roll backwards. Beesley ran after them and managed to apply the hand brake. As they slid to a stop the cars tipped over — crushing Beesley underneath them. But dozens of people inside the train cars were saved by his actions. It was a heroic end to a heroic life.

On August 19, 2007, I was in Dieppe for the 65th anniversary commemoration of the raid. The whole town was draped in Canadian flags. It was the most moving experience I have ever had as a Canadian. I also met many of the men whose stories are told in my non-fiction book on the raid, *DIEPPE: Canada's Darkest Day of World War II*.

I've been lucky enough to write about some of history's more exciting stories. In 1986 I worked with Dr. Robert Ballard, the explorer who found the lost wreck of the *Titanic*, on his bestselling book, *The Discovery of the Titanic*. A few years later, I wrote two books about the ever-fascinating doomed ship: *Inside the Titanic*, and *882½ Amazing Answers to Your Questions About the Titanic*.

In 1993 I was privileged to be able to examine the diaries, letters and photo albums of the last tsar of Russia and his family. From this came the book *Anastasia's Album*. Other books I have written include: *Carnation, Lily, Lily, Rose*; *To Be a Princess*; *The Other Mozart* and *Breakout Dinosaurs*.

* * *

Hugh Brewster is the award-winning author of eleven books. His many awards include the Children's Literature Roundtables of Canada Information Book Award for *On Juno Beach*; the Norma Fleck Award for Children's Non-Fiction for *At Vimy Ridge*; a nomination for the Governor General's Award for *Carnation, Lily, Lily, Rose;* a Silver Birch Award nomination for *DIEPPE: Canada's Darkest Day of World War II;* and Silver Birch and Red Cedar Awards for *Anastasia's Album*. More information about Hugh Brewster is available on his website.

Author's Acknowledgments

I would like to acknowledge the help of Dieppe veterans and their families in sharing their memories and mementoes. Ron Reynolds provided regular inspiration and information for this book and I am greatly indebted to him and his wife, Margaret. Fred Engelbrecht, a veteran of the RHLI, also has an excellent memory and store of fascinating stories. I'd also like to thank RHLI veteran Gordon McPartlin for his recollections and also Jayne Poolton-Turvey, who worked with her father, the late Jack Poolton, on his memoir, *Destined to Survive: A Dieppe Veteran's Story*. Another book to which I'm indebted, particularly for accounts of life in prison camp, is John Mellor's *Forgotten Heroes*. Captain Bruce Barbeau at the Royal Regiment Museum read the manuscript and provided a host of excellent suggestions including the words to the "Basher's Dashers" song. Thanks also to Stan Overy of the Royal Hamilton Light Infantry Heritage Museum and filmmaker Terence Macartney-Filgate for their photograph collections. Special thanks go to military historian J. L. Granatstein for his expert read of the text and to my long-time colleague and editor, Sandra Bogart Johnston.

Other books in the
I AM CANADA Series

Blood and Iron
Building the Railway
Paul Yee

Coming in 2011

Shot at Dawn
World War I
John Wilson

Deadly Voyage
R.M.S. *Titanic*
Hugh Brewster

For more information please see the I AM CANADA
website: www.scholastic.ca/iamcanada